14/12/05

Community Care Tragedies:
A Practice Guide to Mental Health Inquiries

Margaret Reith

VENTURE PRESS

Reprinted 2000

Published by
VENTURE PRESS
16 Kent Street
Birmingham
B5 6RD

British Library Cataloguing-in-Publication Data
A catalogue record for this book is available from the British Library

ISBN 1 873878 51 6   (paperback)

Cover design by:
Western Arts
194 Goswell Road
London
EC1V 7DT

Printed in Great Britain

In memory of Justin

without whose inspiration and wisdom
this book would never have been written

Contents   Page

Tables

Acknowledgements

This book is committed to learning how to develop good practice and improve mental health services by integrating and collating the wealth of information from mental health inquiries. I am deeply indebted to many people who have encouraged and sustained me as my quest to achieve this has emerged. Unfortunately it is not possible to mention everyone and my appreciation goes to all who have contributed in whatever way.

I particularly want to thank all my colleagues in the South Wales Forensic Psychiatric Service who have supported me, especially my long-suffering social work team, Margaret, Martin, Andrea and Penny, also Gordon at Bridgend County Borough Council who has consistently encouraged me with his own enthusiasm for the project. An enormous thank you to both my secretaries for their crucial contribution: Mel for patiently helping me to overcome my computer phobia and Ann for her help with collating the recommendations and much more. Her dedication to the task has been invaluable, both her persistence in the pursuit of copyright permissions and her willingness to devote her own time to the final presentation.

I would like also to thank my many supporters throughout the UK mental health services who have contributed so much in so many different ways, especially Pattie from the Forensic Social Work Group of the British Association of Social Workers and Michael from the Social Services Inspectorate at the Department of Health.

My own learning has been enhanced immeasurably by the thoughtful questions and stimulating comments offered me by the many audiences provided by my teaching opportunities. Being invited to provide joint training alongside my multi-professional colleagues at Caswell Clinic has reinforced my commitment to multidisciplinary team work. My particular thanks to Chris, Tegwyn and Rowena for their suggestions and constructive criticism. I wish also to thank my patients, both those in hospital and in the community, who have taught me so much and whose ideas and thoughtful comments I hope I have heeded.

Lastly, a special thank you to my children, Emma and Tim, who have remained uncomplaining while being forced to learn to cook, even if their new-found skills have not always extended to the washing up, and of course to Malcolm for the suggestions and clarity he has brought to the book, but especially for his belief in my ability to write it.

By bringing together the recommendations from a substantial number of inquiries and indexing them, together with drawing out the significant findings, I hope that the book will provide a useful resource for mental health practitioners, planners, policy-makers and students. In some small way, such a resource may contribute to a better future for those people suffering from severe mental health problems as well as indirectly for those closest to them. As I reach the concluding stages of writing I am acutely aware of how much I have left out and how much more there is to learn. Several reports have been published after I have reached my self-imposed deadline, and each one adds to the debate about how to achieve a better quality of life while ensuring public safety. My overriding feeling as I reach this stage of my own learning and writing is one of humility. The generosity of my colleagues, patients, friends and family has led me to hope that this small contribution to the whole will be somehow worthwhile, but the responsibility for the book's inadequacies remains my own.

Margaret Reith
Cardiff

The author and publishers wish to thank the following who have kindly given permission for the use of copyright material:

Camden & Islington Health Authority from 'The Report into the Care and Treatment of Martin Mursell', published March 1997.

Camden & Islington Health Authority from 'Learning Lessons: Report into the events leading to the incident at St John's Way Medical Centre in December 1995', published December 1996.

City of Westminster, Kensington & Chelsea and Westminster Health Authority, and the North West London Mental Health NHS Trust from 'Independent Panel of Inquiry into the circumstances surrounding the deaths of Ellen and Alan Boland', published March 1995.

Dorset Health Commission from 'The Report of the Independent Inquiry into the circumstances surrounding the deaths of Robert and Muriel Viner', published March 1996.

Ealing, Hammersmith & Hounslow Health Authority and the London Borough of Hounslow from 'Report of the Independent Inquiry Team into the Care and Treatment of NG', published April 1996.

East London & The City Health Authority from 'Report of the Independent Team into the Care and Treatment of Kenneth Grey to East London & the City Health Authority', published November 1995.

Gerald Duckworth and Company Limited from 'The Case of Jason Mitchell: Report of the Independent Panel of Inquiry', published April 1996.

Gerald Duckworth and Company Limited from 'Report of the Committee of Inquiry into the events leading up to and surrounding the fatal incident at the Edith Morgan Centre, Torbay on 1 September 1993'.

Haringey Area Child Protection Committee from 'Inquiry into the Deaths of Jason and Natalia Harry', published September 1994 (Summary Report).

HMSO from 'The Report of the Inquiry into the Care and Treatment of Christopher Clunis' , published February 1994. Crown copyright is reproduced with the permission of the Controller of Her Majesty's Stationery Office.

HMSO from 'Report of the Committee of Inquiry into the Care and After-Care of Miss Sharon Campbell', published July 1988. Crown copyright is reproduced with the permission of the Controller of Her Majesty's Stationery Office.

Leicestershire Health Authority from 'Report of the Independent Inquiry into the Treatment and Care of Richard John Burton', published October 1996.

Mental Welfare Commission for Scotland from 'Report of the Inquiry into the Care and Treatment of Philip McFadden', published August 1995.

North East Thames Regional Health Authority from 'Independent Inquiry Kevin Rooney', published December 1992.

Northumberland Health Authority from 'Report to Northumberland Health Authority of the Independent Inquiry Team into the Care and Treatment of Richard Stoker', published December 1996.

North West London Mental Health NHS Trust from 'The Report of the Independent Panel of Inquiry examining the Case of Michael Buchanan', published November 1994.

Nottingham Health Authority from 'Report of the Inquiry Panel set up by Nottingham Health Authority to Investigate the Serious Untoward Incident at the Tudor Rest Home, West Bridgford, on the night of 3/4 August 1993', published November 1993.

Oxfordshire Health Authority from 'Report of the Inquiry into the circumstances leading to the death of Jonathan Newby (a volunteer worker) on the 9 October 1993 in Oxford', published July 1995.

Redbridge & Waltham Forest Health Authority from 'Report of the Independent Inquiry into the Care and Treatment of Kumbi Mabota to Redbridge & Waltham Forest Health Authority', published September 1996.

Redbridge & Waltham Forest Health Authority from 'Report of the Independent Inquiry Team into the Care and Treatment of Francis Hampshire', published May 1996.

Southern Derbyshire Health Authority and Derbyshire County Council from 'Report of the Inquiry into the Care of Anthony Smith', published October 1996.

Tees Health Authority from 'Caring for the Carer: Report of the Committee of Inquiry to Tees Health Authority', published September 1996.

Tees Health Authority from 'Report of the Inquiry into the Care and Treatment of Shaun Anthony Armstrong', published June 1996.

Trent Health Authority from 'Regional Fact Finding Committee of Enquiry into the Admission, Care, Treatment and Discharge of Carol Barratt', published October 1991.

Western Health and Social Services Board from 'Report of the Inquiry Team to the Western Health and Social Services Board', published October 1995.

West Kent Health Authority and Kent County Council Social Services from 'Report of the Inquiry into the Treatment and Care of Raymond Sinclair', published June 1996.

West Midlands Regional NHS Executive from 'Report of the Panel of Inquiry Appointed to Investigate the Case of Kim Kirkman', published November 1991.

Every effort has been made to trace all the copyright holders but if any have been inadvertently overlooked, the publishers will be pleased to make the necessary arrangements at the first opportunity.

Material in chapter 3 entitled 'Risk Assessment and Risk Management' first appeared as an article in *Medicine, Science and Law* Volume 38, No. 2. Copyright is with the British Academy of Forensic Sciences.

Material in chapter 4 entitled 'Implication for Probation Practice' first appeared in *Probation Journal* Volume 44, No. 2. Copyright is with Probation Journal.

Chapter 1
Introduction

Within the sphere of mental health services, the 1990s will be remembered for the massive shift in the way society cares for those people with severe mental health problems and the tragedies which have sometimes followed. The hospital downsizing programme of the 1980s has gathered momentum which has led to increasing evidence of the difficulties of organising and delivering quality services in the community instead of traditional institutional care. When care in the community has had tragic outcomes this has rightly led to searching questions being asked. The problems which have beset community care have been seized upon by a largely unsympathetic public and fuelled by the media always eager to sensationalise society's problems. Several high profile cases have highlighted the weaknesses and deficits in the way care in the community is provided. The safety net, such as it is, seems to contain many holes. However, in some cases it is claimed that it was not a case of slipping through the net, 'the problem was that . . . there was no net' (Joughin, 1997, para. 2.55).

The government of the day responded to this pressure, in an attempt to reassure the electorate that public safety was its overriding concern, by introducing a series of measures designed to calm fears and restore public confidence that those with severe mental health problems could be cared for safely in the community. By 1992, the government commissioned the Royal College of Psychiatrists to undertake the first national investigation into homicides committed by people with a known mental health history. The remit was extended at the request of the psychiatrists to include suicides (Boyd, 1996).

Particular tragic events, such as the mauling to death by a lion at London Zoo of Ben Silcock in December 1992 and the death of Jonathan Zito who was stabbed in the London Underground by Christopher Clunis in the same month in that year, attracted a large amount of public disquiet which could not be ignored by central government. These events as well as others prompted the government to issue guidance in 1994 to health authorities and social services departments under the heading of 'If things go wrong' requiring an independent inquiry in particular circumstances (NHS Executive, 1994, paras. 33-36). 'In cases of homicide, it will always be necessary to hold an inquiry which is independent of the providers involved' (NHSE, 1994, para. 34). Since this guidance was issued there have been an increasing number of reports published, probably not because of any increase in the number of homicides but owing to this requirement.

The guidance outlines the remit of the inquiry, the composition of its panel, and the distribution of the report. It was revised slightly in 1995 in 'Building Bridges' (Department of Health, 1995). The more recent reports are building on the work of earlier ones allowing the development of a framework for understanding the complexities and problems inherent in delivering mental health services. For example, the Sinclair Inquiry (1996) extends the risk factors identified in the Kirkman Inquiry (1991) to provide a more comprehensive understanding of risk assessment. The Campbell Inquiry (1988, rec. 22) suggests joint health and social services responsibility to provide after-care which was subsequently translated into the Care Programme Approach and receives much greater attention in subsequent inquiries, for example, Taylor (1996). Similarly both Campbell (1988, rec. 26) and Clunis (1994, rec. 37) identify the need for Supervision Registers which were introduced in England in 1994 (Department of Health, 1994b). The Buchanan Inquiry (1994, rec. 15) develops ideas around the working of the supervision register by suggesting that there should be a specially designated supervision register team. Each particular tragedy is investigated in order that underlying reasons can be understood and any necessary improvements to policy and practice can be made. The findings are presented together with recommendations with a view to preventing similar tragedies from occurring in the future.

This book puts the inquiries into context by giving a policy perspective and examines the role and function as well as some of the problems of the inquiry process. Chapter Two lists the reports in date order of publication with a brief synopsis outlining the background to each inquiry. The recommendations are reproduced in full in order to ensure completeness. To enhance the usefulness of the recommendations they are indexed separately and cross-referenced in the accompanying text. Producing such a comprehensive index represents a significant innovation. With the exception of the inquiries chaired by Blom-Cooper (1995 and 1996), even individual inquiry reports contain no index of their recommendations. Chapter Three contains six sections which draw out the implications from each inquiry for the professions receiving most attention in the reports. These sections include psychiatry, community nursing, hospital nursing, social work, probation, and general practice. Most reports have not addressed extensively the issues for psychology or occupational therapy, so although the contribution from these professions remains a valuable part of individual treatment, they are not dealt with separately here.

Chapter Four identifies important issues which recur throughout the reports and which have repeatedly concerned inquiry teams. The four main issues considered include risk assessment and management, race, ethnicity, and cultural sensitivity,

Section 117 Aftercare and the Care Programme Approach, and housing. The last chapter brings together the main points, showing how communication and working across disciplines and agencies are central to successful community-based mental health services. It also suggests other ways forward as an alternative to the present dependence on inquiries as a mechanism for improving practice and achieving change.

The role of inquiries

What is the proper role of inquiries into mental health tragedies? Are there benefits to be gained from the publication of this proliferation of reports and, if so, what are they? Is the number of reports causing public alarm without strengthening confidence in the provision of community care? By focusing so much attention on the very small minority of people with a severe mental illness who pose a risk to other people's safety, the overall picture of services for those suffering with mental health problems becomes distorted. The Royal College of Psychiatrists Confidential Inquiry into Homicides and Suicides by Mentally Ill People indicates that 'there is a small but significant increased risk of violence by mentally ill people, notably those with psychotic disorders, particularly schizophrenia . . . homicide is uncommon'. This report shows from other research evidence that 'people with schizophrenia were one hundred more times likely to kill themselves than others' (Boyd, 1996, p82) Moreover, the much larger number of homicides committed by people who are not diagnosed as mentally ill and who therefore receive prison sentences goes largely unnoticed by the media. The same inquiry examines the statistics using the legal distinction of 'normal' and 'abnormal' homicides. The study concludes that of the convictions for homicide in England and Wales (between 450 and 500 annually over the last 10 years) approximately 80 per cent were legally normal (Boyd, 1996, p81).

Are inquiry reports the best way to achieve improvements in practice or should policy and practice be driven by other, more considered mechanisms? The mental health inquiry reports which have arisen as a result of tragedies in community care in the 1990s are intended at least in part to enable mistakes to be rectified and lessons to be learnt. However, the number of such reports is militating against assimilation of their contents for policy makers and practitioners.

A brief historical perspective

Until the late 1980s mental health inquiry reports focused exclusively on the scandals of bad practice that were identified in many of the long-stay psychiatric and mental handicap institutions. A useful perspective to the current picture is provided by Martin's work on mental health inquiry reports arising from disasters in hospital care (Martin, 1984). His study of earlier inquiries into hospital mal-practice considers in detail 22 hospital-based inquiries between 1968 and 1981 and argues that such attention to deficiencies in institutional services does in fact achieve change.

Martin concludes that despite the financial implications and pain arising from inquiries collectively they do achieve improvement in services. However, improvements in hospital care did not follow investigations into poor practice automatically. 'The most disturbing thing about these reports is that, to a large extent, they pointed to conditions that were already known about' (Martin, 1984, p60). This could equally be said of the reports of today. One of the problems identified by Martin was that there was no mechanism by which the lessons of a particular inquiry could be generalised and applied elsewhere. This remains a difficulty for current inquiries. Then, as now, inquiries were locally driven with individual health authorities having little power to effect change on a broader scale. 'The failure to absorb the lessons of inquiries and spread their results effectively is not surprising, given their local origins (and often very limited circulation) and above all, the difficulties the DHSS has in communicating with Districts' (Martin, 1984, p71). As for the DHSS using its power to promote important policy changes, Martin argues convincingly that the DHSS had a different agenda largely driven by the need to limit demand for additional resources which would have been an inevitable outcome of insisting on wide-spread improvements to hospital care. 'There are, therefore, powerful structural and political reasons why the lessons are not spread as enthusiastically as the lay observer might expect' (Martin, 1984, p71).

Although these earlier inquiries were very different in their focus, it is the fact that they took place that has been partly responsible for the policy of discharging patients from hospital (or not admitting them in the first place) to the community. The solution to an earlier set of problems created within closed institutions was seen as being community care. The concept of community care was idealised, with issues of public safety and the need for intensive support services being either over-simplified or disregarded. Risk assessment as it is known today and the safe management of risk in the community have only become a necessity since large numbers of people who would previously have been cared for in hospital are now living outside. Resource and training inadequacies arising from insufficient under-standing of the complexities of providing care in the community and difficulties in transferring funding from hospital-based to community-based services followed. Some of the consequences of this have led to a different kind of tragedy which in turn has resulted in public outcry and media criticism demanding investigation. According to Grounds, 'The challenge for community psychiatric care has been to work out how to provide the multiple functions of the hospital outside an institutional framework. . . However, providing the functional equivalent of public protection, control and containment is an unsolved challenge' (Grounds, 1995, p 46).

Learning from inquiries

Finding ways of meeting these challenges remains the task of policy makers, managers, and mental health practitioners. The framework for providing community-based services is still less than adequate. But how do mental health professionals develop their services in the light of recent inquiries? 'Practitioners who do not address the need for change in their own practices, disempower service users' (Woodley, 1995, p160). The lessons to be gained from the analysis an inquiry offers into a mental health tragedy can be far more powerful than the more theoretical perspectives offered by many textbooks. Despite the inherent weaknesses of reports such as the bias of hindsight, it would be foolish to disregard them. Moreover, if the rules governing inquiries do not change it is only a matter of time before most mental health managers and practitioners will be subjected to the inquiry process.

There is little point in holding an expensive independent inquiry into a 'community care' tragedy unless the lessons are learnt. Mental health workers need to change their own policies and practices in the light of this scrutiny and should not be complacent by ignoring service deficiencies elsewhere. Petch and Bradley consider that 'it should not be necessary for every authority in the country to have its own homicide inquiry and report before learning lessons and embarking on an action plan to remedy the situation at local level' (Petch and Bradley, 1997, p 162).

However, the sheer number makes learning from inquiry reports a daunting prospect. They can be difficult to obtain, and the absence of a co-ordinated list increases this particular problem, although the work of Sheppard, developed by Sheppard and Edwards in listing reports on the Internet, is useful in this respect (Sheppard, 1996 and Sheppard and Edwards). The confusion is compounded by the inconsistent approach taken in naming reports, resulting in most of them being known by the name of the mentally disordered offender, for example the Buchanan Report (1994). However, others are named after the victim as in the Newby Report. The rationale for such a title is explained by the Chair, Nicola Davies. 'The life that was lost was that of Jonathan Newby. We considered that the only name which could appear in the title to this report should be his' (Newby, 1995, p 7).

Some reports strive hard to avoid identification of the mentally disordered offender. This approach is based on sound principles but adds to the difficulties in identifying reports. Camden & Islington Health Authority which published the report 'Learning Lessons' (1996), chaired by Rosemary Nicholson, wishes to ensure that there is no mention of any individual involved in the incident in the title. I have therefore followed the practice used by the Woodley Report (1995) and refer to it by the name of its Chair. Although the Woodley Report (1995) is named in this way in order to anonymise it, other reports do so by using the initials of the offender in the title (for example the NG report, 1996). Another report avoids using the name of the individual with an unwieldy title which refers to a '. . . serious untoward incident at the Tudor Rest Home . . .'. For consistency I refer to it as the DU inquiry, 1993. These last three reports strive to avoid all reference to individuals by name, a practice that I strongly endorse, although it makes for cumbersome annotation. Despite the ethically sound intentions of such inquiry teams, anonymity is not always consistently achieved and in any case press coverage of the case invariably sabotages the process. Interestingly, Blom-Cooper's inquiry, 'The Falling Shadow', does not reveal its victim's name or the offender's or the name of the Chair in its title (Blom-Cooper, 1995). An additional source of confusion is that reports are sometimes referred to in more than one form so that for example, the Clunis Inquiry (1994) is also called the 'Ritchie Report' after its Chair, Jean Ritchie QC.

To try to make sense of the plethora of inquiry reports of the 1990s, with their confusing titles and sources of publication, Table 1 entitled 'Mental Health Inquiry Reports' lists 28 inquiry reports in date order of publication. (*Table 1 follows on pages 8, 9 and 10*) All hospital-based inquiries have been excluded, such as the 'Ashworth Inquiry' (Blom-Cooper, 1992) and the 'Orville Blackwood Inquiry' (Blackwood, 1993), not because they are not important but in order to focus on the care of the severely mentally ill person in the community. Despite the offence having occurred in hospital, the Robinson report (Blom-Cooper, 1995) is considered because of the emphasis it places on community care issues.

The reports evaluated are all from the 1990s with one exception. The inquiry into the death of social worker Isabel Schwarz, which published its report in 1988, has been included because it is the first significant report into a tragedy of community care and is therefore important from a historical perspective for the purposes of clarity (Campbell, 1988). It also provides useful comparative data. The somewhat primitive level of community-based services for people with severe mental health problems, the limited understanding of risk assessment and its relative importance as well as the inadequacies of inter-agency and multidisciplinary communication identified in this report constitute reminders of the progress that has been made in service development. Another report that is included because of its important messages involves a serious incident that did not have a fatal outcome (Nicholson, 1996).

One report not included in the table but which is nevertheless useful is that of Joughin which is concerned with a mother who killed her younger daughter and attempted to kill the elder one. This report makes many important observations about services and contains over 200 recommendations which pertain specifically to the Isle of Man (Joughin, 1997). More recently, the Carr report examined the difficulties of providing effective services in the community for people suffering from personality disorders (Carr, 1997). It makes 14 recommendations which are referred to in the relevant sections within each chapter. Similarly, the Kopernik-Steckel Inquiry (1997), the Howell Inquiry (1997), and the Holland Inquiry (1997) are referred to in the text. The Howell Inquiry was commissioned because David Howell was shot dead by police in November 1996 while receiving care and treatment from both his local health and social services authorities. The Holland Inquiry differs from others because it is not one of homicide but reflects public unease after Mr Holland, who had a history of sexual offences against children, absconded from an escorted leave to a zoo which shared an entrance to a theme park.

Problems with inquiries
There are many criticisms of the whole inquiry process and many would argue that it is not an effective way of improving services, that the lessons are not being learnt, and that the costs outweigh the benefits. Eastman, for example, considers that inquiries 'are inherently ill-suited to looking into service levels and operation in a detailed way; these are far better addressed by "service audit"'. (Eastman, 1996, pp157-8). The process of holding independent inquiries is very expensive. Also there have now been so many that, apart from having a direct impact on the local services related to the inquiry, they are less likely to inform policy making more generally. On a purely local basis the impact of an inquiry continues to be considerable. For example, the Viner Report (1996) is a response to a tragedy which occurred in Dorset and has resulted in significant changes to policy and practice in Dorset in relation to the assessment of carers' needs and the rights of carers to have an independent assessment. However, it is questionable to what extent corresponding change has occurred elsewhere. Unusually, Croydon

Table 1. Mental Health Inquiry Reports

Report Name as Published	Chair of Report	Inquiry Title	Victim	Offender	Date Published	Publisher
Sharon Campbell Inquiry	John Spokes QC	Report of the Committee of Inquiry into the Care and After-Care of Miss Sharon Campbell	Isabel Schwarz (social worker)	Sharon Campbell	July 1988	HMSO, CM 440
Carol Barratt Inquiry	Cyril Unwin MBE, JP	Regional Fact Finding Committee of Inquiry into the Admission, Care, Treatment and Discharge of Carol Barratt	An 11-year-old girl	Carol Barratt	October 1991	Trent Health Authority
Kim Kirkman Inquiry	Dr Donald Dick	Report of the Panel of Inquiry Appointed to Investigate the Case of Kim Kirkham	Elizabeth Ford (neighbour)	Kim Kirkham	November 1991	West Midlands Regional Health Authority
Rooney Inquiry	Andrew Collins QC	Independent Inquiry – Kevin Rooney	Grace Quigley (girlfriend)	Kevin Rooney	December 1992	North East Thames Regional Health Authority
The DU Inquiry	Mrs P Turnbull	Report of the Inquiry Panel to Investigate the Serious Untoward Incident at the Tudor Rest Home, West Bridgford, on the night of 3rd/4th August 1993	Mr V (resident of nursing home)	DU	November 1993	Nottingham Health Authority
Clunis Inquiry	Jean Ritchie QC	The Report of the Inquiry into the Care and Treatment of Christopher Clunis	Jonathan Zito (stranger)	Christopher Clunis	February 1994	HMSO N/E Thames Health Authority S/E Thames Health Authority
Harry Inquiry	Jean Gabbott	Inquiry into the Deaths of Jason and Natalia Harry	Jason and Natalia Harry (son and daughter)	Sharon D	September 1994 Summary Report	Haringey Area Child Protection Committee
Buchanan Inquiry	Christopher Heginbotham	The Report of the Independent Panel of Inquiry Examining the Case of Michael Buchanan	Frederick Graver (stranger)	Michael Buchanan	November 1994	North West London Mental Health Trust
The Falling Shadow	Louis Blom-Coooper QC	Report of the Committee of Inquiry into the events leading up to and surrounding the fatal incident at the Edith Morgan Centre, Torbay on 1st September 1993	Georgina Robinson (no relation) occupational therapist	Andrew Robinson	January 1995	Duckworth
Boland Inquiry	Mrs J Hughes	Independent Panel of Inquiry into the Circumstances Surrounding the Deaths of Ellen and Alan Boland	Ellen Boland (mother)	Alan Boland	March 1995	City of Westminster, the Kensington & Chelsea and Westminster Health Authorities, and the North West London Mental Health NHS Trust

Report Name as Published	Chair of Report	Inquiry Title	Victim	Offender	Date Published	Publisher
Newby Report	Nicola Davies QC	Report of the Inquiry into the circumstances leading to the death of Jonathan Newby on 9th October 1993 in Oxford	Jonathan Newby (care worker)	John Rous	July 1995	Oxfordshire Health Authority
McFadden Inquiry	Dr James Dyer	Report of the Inquiry into the Care and Treatment of Philip McFadden	Lewis Felton (policeman)	Philip McFadden	August 1995	Mental Welfare Commission for Scotland
Woodley Team Report	Len Woodley QC	Report of the Independent Review Panel to East London and the City Health Authority and Newham Council	BB (mental health service user)	SL	September 1995	East London & the City Health Authority
The Brian Doherty Inquiry	Professor George Fenton	Report of the Inquiry Team to the Western Health and Social Services Board	Kieran Hegarty (stranger)	Brian Doherty	October 1995	Western Health and Social Services Board
The Grey Report	Jane Mishcon	Report of the Independent Inquiry Team into the Care and Treatment of Kenneth Grey to East London and the City Health Authority	Leonie McGlashan (mother)	Kenneth Grey	November 1995	East London & the City Health Authority
The Viner Report	Anthony Harbour	The Report of the Independent Inquiry into the circumstances surrounding the deaths of Robert and Muriel Viner	Muriel Viner (mother)	Robert Viner	March 1996	Dorset Health Commission
Jason Mitchell Inquiry	Louis Blom-Cooper QC	The Case of Jason Mitchell: Report of the Independent Panel of Inquiry	Arthur & Shirley Wilson (strangers) Robert Mitchell (father)	Jason Mitchell	April 1995	Duckworth
NG Inquiry	John Main QC	Report of the Independent Inquiry Team into the Care and Treatment of NG	SJ (stranger)	NG	April 1996	Ealing, Hammersmith & Hounslow Health Authority
The Hampshire Report	Jane Mishcon	Report of the Independent Inquiry Team into the Care and Treatment of Francis Hampshire	Catherine Hampshire (wife)	Francis Hampshire	May 1996	Redbridge & Waltham Forest Health Authority
Armstrong Inquiry	Mr C J Freeman	Report of the Inquiry into the Care and Treatment of Shaun Anthony Armstrong	Rosie Palmer (child)	Shaun Armstrong	June 1995	Tees District Health Authority

Report Name as Published	Chair of Report	Inquiry Title	Victim	Offender	Date Published	Publisher
Sinclair Inquiry	Richard Lingham	Report of the Inquiry into the Treatment and Care of Raymond Sinclair	Mary Povey (mother)	Raymond Sinclair	June 1996	West Kent Health Authority and Kent County Council Social Services
The Mabota Report	Derek Holwill	Report of the Independent Inquiry Team into the Care and Treament of Kumbi Mabota to Redbridge and Waltham Forset Health Authority	Lidie Njoli Diema (girlfriend)	Kumbi Mabota	September 1996	Redbridge & Waltham Forest Health Authority
Caring for the Carer	Richard Barlow	Caring for the Carer: Report of the Committee of Inquiry to Tees Health Authority	William Taylor (father)	Keith Taylor	September 1996	Tees Health Authority
Smith Inquiry	Professor Sir John Wood	Report of the Inquiry into the Care of Anthony Smith	Gwendoline Smith (mother) David Smith (half-brother)	Anthony Smith	October 1996	Southern Derbyshire Health Authority and Derbyshire County Council
Burton Inquiry	Hugh Chapman	Report of the Independent Inquiry into the Treatment and Care of Richard John Burton	Janice Symons (landlady)	Richard Burton	October 1996	Leicestershire Health Authority
Stoker Inquiry	Mr A G Brown	Report to Northumberland Health Authority of the Independent Inquiry into the Care and Treatment of Richard Stoker	Halina Szymczuk (mental health service user)	Richard Stoker	December 1996	Northumberland Health Authority
Learning Lessons	Ms Rosemary Nicholson	Learning Lessons: Report into the events leading to the incident at St John's Way Medical Centre in December 1995	Dr Inwald GP (not fatal)	Maria Caseiro	December 1996	Camden & Islington Health Authority
Mursell Inquiry	Lincoln Crawford	The Report into the Care and Treatment of Martin Mursell	Joe and Mary Collins (step-father) (mother - not fatal)	Martin Mursell	March 1997	Camden & Islington Health Authority

Health Authority circulated the Kopernik-Steckel Inquiry (1997) widely because of a recognition of the need to learn from it. Sometimes, instead of achieving a critical analysis of services it is argued that inquiries are merely able to apportion blame. In the words of Carson, inquiries 'are about blaming, not just learning'. (Carson, 1996, p 124). Similarly, child abuse inquiries were often seen as being preoccupied with blaming individual practitioners. Reder and Duncan comment that 'understanding complex cases requires an approach that goes beyond blaming'(Reder and Duncan, 1996, p82).

One of the long-term consequences of published reports which is often over-looked is that, in the future when some of the subjects of inquiries are mentally stable and could be rehabilitated, it may prove impossible to achieve this because the person's identity will be so well known. Other criticisms of the inquiry process are the huge cost, both financial and personal, and the inevitable tendency for inquiry findings to be biased by hindsight. It is all too easy to arrive at a con-clusion based on making the wrong correlations between interrelated factors. It is certainly often argued that there have now been enough inquiries, and the require-ment that they should be held following a homicide committed by a mentally disordered offender should be reconsidered. Eastman is quite clear on this point: 'It is time to abolish mandatory inquiries into psychiatric homicides . . . there is no evidence that inquiries do much more than duplicate the findings of their prede-cessors. Nor is there evidence that there is an accumulated body of knowledge arising out of inquiries that has resulted in improved care' (Eastman, 1996, p170). Comparisons with the problems encountered in child protection inquiries following deaths of children from abuse are often made, generally with the sug-gestion that it is now time in the field of mental health to review the problems the inquiry culture has generated and adopt a way forward not dissimilar from the Area Child Protection Committees.

Another aspect of inquiries sometimes promoted as a valid reason for their existence is that to some extent they do address or at least recognise the needs of the victim's family. The Kopernik-Steckel Inquiry team 'hope that [their] report will elucidate what happened and provide some of the answers [the family] are looking for' (Kopernik-Steckel, 1997, p2). Rock maintains that 'what survivors want is a combination of reforms centred on practical and symbolic matters' (Rock, 1996, p117). The expression of anger and intense grief of the victims' families needs to be taken seriously. One way of addressing this is by allowing a full investigation of the facts, although it does not necessarily ensure that people feel adequately helped in the face of such overwhelming personal tragedy. There have been several occasions recently when victims' relatives have not been satisfied with the findings of the inquiry team. For example, the mother of Rosie

Palmer, a three-year-old killed by Shaun Armstrong, is reported as saying that the report was 'a whitewash' and that she did not accept that Rosie's death 'could not have been predicted' as is claimed by the Armstrong inquiry report (Cooper, 1996). More recently it has been reported that Rosie's mother is to sue the health authority and hospital trust for alleged neglect – 'the failure to diagnose, treat and assess Armstrong properly' (The Independent, 5 August 1997, p2).

One of the features that is highlighted by Table 1.1, and developed in Table 1. 2, is that it is possible at a glance to identify the victims. Thus, of the 28 reports considered, 15 of the victims were either close relatives or carers (six were mothers): five were professional carers; seven were neighbours or other mental health service users, and 10 were strangers. In some cases, the victim falls into more than one category – for example, the victim in 'Learning Lessons' was a general practitioner but also a stranger. It should be noted that in this case the outcome of the incident was not fatal (Nicholson, 1996).

Table 2   Relationships of Victims with Mentally Disordered Offenders

Offender	Victim	Relative/ Carer	Professional/ Care worker	Neighbour / User	Stranger
Sharon Campbell	Isabel Schwarz		Social Worker		
Carol Barratt	Emma Brodie				Child
Kim Kirkman	Elizabeth Ford			Neighbour	
Kevin Rooney	Grace Quigley	Girlriend		User	
DU	Mr V			User	
Christopher Clunis	Jonathan Zito				Adult
Sharon D	Jason & Natalia Harry	Son & Daughter			
Michael Buchanan	Frederick Graver				Adult
Andrew Robinson	Georgina Robinson (no relation)		Occupational Therapist		
Alan Boland	Ellen Boland	Mother/Carer			
John Rous	Jonathan Newby		Care Worker		
Philip Mc Fadden	Lewis Fulton		Policeman		Adult
SL	BB			User	

Table 2 continued

Offender	Victim	Relative/ Carer	Professional/ Care worker	Neighbour / User	Stranger
Brian Doherty	Kieran Hegarty				Child
Kenneth Grey	Leonie McGlashan	Mother			
Robert Viner	Muriel Viner	Mother/Carer			
Jason Mitchell	Robert Mitchell Arthur Wilson Shirley Wilson	Father			Adult Adult
NG	SJ				Adult
Francis Hampshire	Catherine Hampshire	Wife/Carer			
Shaun Armstrong	Rosie Palmer			Neighbour	Child
Raymond Sinclair	Mary Povey	Mother/Carer			
Kumbi Mabota	Lidie Njoli Diema	Girl-friend			
Keith Taylor	William Taylor	Father			
Anthony Smith	Gwendoline Smith David Smith	Mother/Carer Half-brother			
Richard Burton	Janice Symons			Landlady	
Richard Stoker	Halina Szymczuk			User	
Maria Caseiro	Dr Inwald (not fatal)		General Practitioner		Adult
Martin Mursell	Joe Collins Mary Collins (not fatal)	Step-father Mother			

13

Chapter 2
Inquiry Reports: Synopses and Recommendations

Introduction

Twenty-eight inquiry reports are listed in date order of publication starting with the earliest. The Chair and members of the inquiry panel are given, in addition to the publisher and date of publication. Each report contains a brief synopsis of its background as well as the outcome, where it is known. Following each synopsis the report's recommendations are reproduced in full with the publishers' permission. Occasionally, I have omitted specific names of health and social services agencies as well as hospitals and teams so that the recommendations have general application and relevance. In many reports the recommendations are contained within the text and are not collated separately. As a result it has been necessary sometimes to simplify the numbering of recommendations in order to ensure consistency of presentation.

It is not my intention to focus on particular local service deficits or difficulties. The purpose in producing a comprehensive set of recommendations is to enable other mental health professionals to reflect on their own situations and learn from the experiences of others. Given the existence of this number of mental health inquiry reports it seems irresponsible not to take account of their findings to improve services. By using inquiries to inform their own practice, policy makers and practitioners alike can take a more proactive approach to service development and good practice. One of my main messages to all involved in providing quality mental health services is that it is possible to be empowered to achieve change by the constructive use of the reports available.

Report of the Committee of Inquiry into the Care and Aftercare of Miss Sharon Campbell.
John Spokes QC (Chair), Dr Michael Pare and George Royle – HMSO Cm 440, July 1988
Synopsis
In 1984 a social worker, Isabel Schwarz, was killed while at work at Bexley Hospital, by a former client of hers, Sharon Campbell, who was then aged 21. Sharon Campbell was found guilty of manslaughter on the grounds of diminished responsibility and detained under Section 37, Mental Health Act 1983 with a restriction order under Section 41 of the Act. Sharon Campbell had a history of mental illness and had been admitted to Bexley Hospital on two previous occasions – in 1980 and 1982. In 1983, while Isabel Schwarz was driving her car,

she was assaulted by Sharon Campbell. As a result of this incident, social work responsibility was transferred from Isabel Schwarz and the hospital social work department of Bexley Social Services to the Social Services Department of Lewisham Council. Meanwhile Isabel Schwarz received telephone threats which were thought to originate from Sharon Campbell. Nine months after the assault Isabel Schwarz was stabbed to death. Sharon Campbell's willingness to engage in supervision and aftercare was variable and her compliance with medication poor. Her mental health appeared to deteriorate when she stopped taking her prescribed medication and contact with services was minimal.

The inquiry's recommendations focus on the importance of providing adequate medical and social work follow-up in the community as well as the minimisation of risk of violence to mental health workers (in this particular case, social workers). This report probably represents the earliest inquiry into the failings of community care. Subsequent guidance such as the Care Programme Approach and the development of Section 117 Aftercare are direct results. Co-ordinating care and maintaining follow-up with patients who are reluctant to comply with treatment plans, and compulsory treatment orders are discussed within the report. The issue of providing ethnically sensitive services is also raised, and the disadvantages experienced by black people within the mental health system are recognised. It seems to be one of the earliest attempts to take account of the needs of ethnic minorities. In addition the report addresses issues relating to housing for people suffering from an enduring mental illness in the community. Risk assessment has yet to be identified as central to successful community care. It is interesting to note the attention devoted to risk assessment and risk management in later inquiries, because it demonstrates the progress that is being made in the rehabilitation of mentally ill people in the community.

Recommendations: Campbell Inquiry

1. Where a patient in a psychiatric hospital is found in possession of a knife or similar weapon, in circumstances where its possession is unauthorised or concealed, a record should be made in the patient's notes of the circumstances and any consequent action.

2. In the interest of patient care, emphasis should continue to be given, in the course of training and supervision of junior doctors, to the importance of recording important information in clinical notes and discharge letters.

3. When a social worker is to take up a post in a hospital multidisciplinary team, there should be discussion between the social work team leader and the consultant psychiatrist to provide information as to the experience of the social worker, so as to assist in deciding what casework the social worker may be asked to undertake, and that from time to time thereafter opportunity should be taken to review the situation.

4. At the time of discharge, the social work plan for the client should be clear and should be recorded in the social work notes. It should also be communicated to others who need, or may need, to know its contents.

5. Social worker supervision should be planned on a basis that the choice of cases for discussion should be that of the supervisor, while, of course, giving the social worker being supervised the opportunity to discuss cases where she or he wants help and advice. The supervisor will need to have a system to ensure that all cases are covered periodically. If there is a requirement for the supervisor to sign the notes read at supervision, the signature should appear at the end of the last note, so that, when next reviewed, the supervisor can readily see what entries have been made since last read.

6. Where a medical practitioner, in giving an opinion, is acting both as the medical officer for an institution and as a medical practitioner for an individual patient, and his or her opinion is influenced by concern for others in the institution as well as the individual patient, the fact that he or she is, or may be, so influenced should be made clear to the patient and recorded in the practitioner's note.

7. The training of social workers should provide guidance on the ways to recognise and if possible avert incidents of violence and that the employing authorities should make written guidelines available.

8. Social workers should be trained and instructed to report incidents of violence and threats of violence and that employing authorities should issue written guidelines on the method of reporting them. Where a central register of incidents is maintained it should be kept up to date.

9. Social work supervision should be conducted so as to emphasise the need to report incidents of violence or threatened violence and so as to elicit if such incidents have occurred.

10. Training and guidance and, where necessary, counselling should be available to social workers to emphasise that, where an incident of violence occurs, this is not necessarily to be looked on as a failure by the social worker and there should be no underlying presumption that the social worker is to blame.

11. Counselling should always be available to social workers who have been victims of serious incidents of violence and that this should be available for a follow-up period extending well beyond the immediate period after the act of violence.

12. While recognising that an incident of violence may be an important matter to discuss at supervision, there should, at the option of the social worker, be someone not normally involved in that supervision available for counselling the social worker following any serious incident of violence affecting the social worker in the course of his or her work.

13. A permanent handover of social work between one authority and another, other than of routine character, should be transferred at not less than team leader level.

14. Local authorities should provide guidelines on supervision which should, in general terms, indicate the scope and purposes of supervision (including scrutiny of records), the intervals at which supervision should occur (varying according to the experience and seniority of the social worker) and the approximate maximum interval that should elapse between consideration of cases held by a social worker.

15. If threats are made or violence used to a social worker by a former client whose case has been transferred to another authority, that authority should be requested (by an officer of the rank of team leader or above) to make inquiries and furnish a report.

16. Social services departments should provide alarm systems in offices to which clients have access so that an audible warning can be sounded at the place where help is needed and so as to give warning to other staff that help is needed.

17. Personal audible alarms should be made available to social workers and support staff if they wish to have them.

18. The layout of social work offices should prevent ready access by clients to areas beyond that in which they are to be interviewed and that, where the layout of the premises is such that it will enhance safety for staff, a separate entrance should be used by social workers who are not accompanied by clients.

19. The layout and decoration of social work offices should take account of the need to provide an atmosphere likely to reduce stress for social work clients.

20. Social services departments should appoint a named individual responsible for oversight of the office security arrangements referred to above and for the periodic testing of alarms and security systems.

21. Consideration should be given as a matter of urgency to the creation of specialist training courses for social workers involved with mentally disordered people, whether in hospital settings or in the community.

22. Health and local authorities, in co-operation with relevant voluntary agencies, should have a duty jointly to provide suitable aftercare for former informal hospital patients who are, or have been, suffering from a mental disorder until those authorities decide jointly that the need no longer exists.

23. The Secretary of State should issue to health and local authorities a written summary clarifying their statutory duties to provide aftercare for formerly mentally disordered hospital patients.

24. The Royal College of Psychiatrists should be invited to publish a document on good practice for discharge and aftercare procedures. Such a document should be published after seeking a consensus with bodies representing nursing, social work, general practitioners, psychology, and occupational therapy.

25. Before discharge from in-patient treatment, a plan should be prepared for a psychiatric patient. The plan should set out the proposals for community care and the time when the plan will come up for review. Such plans will differ widely with circumstances.

26. The Secretary of State should direct district health authorities to establish registers of "designated" patients living in the community and require social services authorities to co-operate with them in providing adequate aftercare. It should be the responsibility of the consultant psychiatrist to keep such a register up to date in his catchment area.

27. Further consideration should be given to forwarding the multidisciplinary approach to care for patients who live in the community. This is likely to be best provided by review at an out-patient clinic or day hospital or a similar community centre for patient care. The review would be attended by the multidisciplinary team, including, where appropriate, the psychiatric consultant and junior doctors, the community psychiatric nurse, the social worker, the occupational therapist, the psychologist, the general practitioner (or an effective link to him or her) and any other staff involved directly in the care of the patient. The rehabilitation or continuing care team forming part of the mental health advice centre, or the out-patient reviews, of which we heard in evidence, may provide a basis for this continuing care in the community. We do not consider it helpful to lay down the interval of time between reviews for individual patients.

28. Further provision should be made for longer-term housing for mentally ill people living in the community, possibly through housing associations, so that, following discharge from hospital, care may be continued beyond the time when the patient is ready to leave the type of short-term hostel accommodation now commonly available.

29. The location of community mental health centres should take account of the needs of ethnic communities.

30. The training of health and social services staff treating and caring for mentally disordered people should take account of the importance of their being able to recognise and respond to the needs of people from differing cultural and ethnic backgrounds.

Regional Fact Finding Committee of Inquiry into the Admission, Care, Treatment and Discharge of Carol Barratt
Cyril Unwin (Chair), Dr D H Morgan and Mr B D M Smith – Doncaster Royal Infirmary Priority and Community Care Services Unit, Trent Regional Health Authority, October 1991
Synopsis
On 16 April 1991 an 11-year-old girl was stabbed and killed in a shopping centre by Carol Barratt. Carol Barratt, who had a long history of psychiatric problems, had been discharged two days previously from the Psychiatric Unit of Doncaster Royal Infirmary. She had been detained under Section 2 of the Mental Health Act 1983 following an incident in which she had threatened a young woman with a knife in the same shopping centre approximately two weeks earlier (30 March 1991).

Five days after this admission (4 April 1991) she attempted to strangle a visitor and was placed on one-to-one observation, but despite such close supervision she managed to abscond and on the same day attacked a girl outside the hospital. Seven days later (11 April 1991), the Mental Health Review Tribunal heard an application for discharge from Carol Barratt but decided not to discharge her from her section. 'She needs supervision at the present time and should not be released from the Section' (Barratt, 1991, para. 19). Three days later (14 April 1991), Carol's mother made a complaint to nursing staff about her care and made demands that she should be discharged from compulsory detention. Following this the Responsible Medical Officer (RMO) agreed to her discharge. The report concludes ' . . . the RMO s decision to terminate her Section thus enabling Carol to discharge herself, and the circumstances in which this decision was made, constituted a serious error of clinical judgement' (Barratt, 1991, para. 27).

Recommendations: Barratt Inquiry

1. The findings of the report as they relate to Carol's RMO should be referred to the regional health authority, as his employing authority, for it to take such action as it thinks fit.

2. The relevant district health authority should examine the medical and nursing standards adopted in the discharge of Carol from her section and take appropriate action.

3. The policy for dealing with disturbed behaviour should be reviewed. The agreed multidisciplinary team levels of observation, and the degree of restriction required to control disturbed patient behaviour, should be carefully spelt out.

4. The nursing and medical responsibility to ensure that patients receive adequate assistance on discharge and immediate follow up support should be reviewed against the background of this case.

5. The role of senior nurses in relation to the evaluation of care needs and monitoring should be reassessed to ensure that sufficient time is spent on the development of clinical nursing models. All staff should receive training in the setting and evaluation of standards.

6. The local health authority should review its approach to the nursing process.

7. The policy on prescribing by telephone should be reviewed.

8. When it has been necessary for any patient to be restrained, a physical examination should be carried out as soon as practicable.

9. The policy and procedures for reporting accidents and untoward incidents should include provision for the earliest practicable notification of all serious occurrences to appropriate senior officers.

10. Sleep patterns should be routinely noted when observation is part of the nursing care plan.

11. A working party should be formed to discuss the nursing and medical interface on roles and responsibilities.

12. Consultant psychiatrists (RMOs) should be reminded that leave for a detained patient should be authorised in writing with appropriate conditions.

13. RMOs submitting medical reports to Mental Health Review Tribunals should make themselves available in person at the hearing wherever practicable.

14. Procedures should require the RMO to give a written order to the managers of a hospital before any patient detained under a section of the Act can be discharged from that section.

15. The local health authority should review the delegation to Officers of Managers' powers and duties under the Mental Health Act.

16. The local police should be asked to review their current practice regarding mentally disordered offenders so that court referrals are considered in appropriate circumstances and invite health authorities and social services departments to contribute to the review.

17. The local health authority should review the facilities for acute mentally ill patients at its Royal Infirmary with the aim of improving the ward layout to facilitate better observation of patients and a better domestic environment.

18. Consideration should be given to the feasibility of providing a locally based secure unit and, perhaps jointly with other authorities, a secure unit to cover the northern area of the Trent region.

Report of the Panel of Inquiry Appointed by the West Midlands Regional Health Authority, South Birmingham Health Authority and the Special Hospitals Service Authority to Investigate the Case of Kim Kirkman
Dr Donald Dick (Chair), Barry Shuttleworth and John Charlton – West Midlands Regional Health Authority, November 1991

Synopsis

In 1990 Kim Kirkman was charged with the murder of Elizabeth Ford, a neighbour. Two months later, at the age of 35, he committed suicide while on remand in prison. For the previous 17 years Kim Kirkman had been compulsorily detained on a hospital order with a restriction order under both the Mental Health Acts of 1959 and 1983. This followed a series of burglaries and assaults which resulted in hospital treatment. Whilst a hospital inpatient, he committed a further assault which resulted in his transfer to a maximum security hospital. He was detained on the grounds that he suffered from psychopathy within the meaning of the Act. He was subsequently transferred to a medium secure unit in 1989, underwent an intensive course of rehabilitation, and received a deferred conditional discharge from the Home Office. Once he had been offered the tenancy of a flat and the other conditions had been met, it was agreed that Kirkman was able to leave hospital. Elizabeth Ford was found murdered on the same day that Kirkman's conditional discharge had been arranged which was 18 months after his transfer from maximum to medium security.

This inquiry presents a comprehensive investigation of the circumstances surrounding the treatment, rehabilitation and aftercare arrangements for Kim Kirkman. It is one of the first reports to contain a detailed consideration of risk assessment, which continues to be referred to in the literature and in government guidance. The inquiry's recommendations are considered under three headings: those which relate to practitioners, those which pertain to government departments, health authorities and service providers and regulators, and finally those which affect research and professional bodies which are concerned with the definition and treatment of psychopathic disorder.

Recommendations: for practitioners – Kirkman Inquiry

1. The clinicians responsible for making decisions about the transfer or discharge of patients should demonstrate that they have checked the original cause for the patient being in hospital, not only the changes in other aspects of the patient's behaviour.

2. All policies which regulate the discharge or transfer of patients should be written, regularly revised, and their outcome subject to regular and automatic clinical audit by clinicians and management.

3. Clinical teams should seek to use the best available actuarial, statistical or predictive techniques to support clinical judgements about dangerousness.

4. Clinical teams should increasingly develop the use of neurophysiological and psychometric tests to support clinical judgements about dangerousness.

5. The responsible medical officer should readily refer to a second consultant opinion before pressing for conditional discharge in doubtful patients. This would offset any good doctor's entirely desirable optimism on the patient's behalf, in contrast to the public's interest.

6. Where the clinical team which is responsible for the discharge and continuing care of a patient asks a housing association or department to provide accommodation for 'a patient at risk', the opinion of a specialist adviser in mental health should always be sought by the housing association.

    Patients at risk for these purposes are those who have been detained in special hospitals in the past, are to be followed up under Section 117 of the Mental Health Act 1983 or the regulations governing the conditional discharge of restricted patients.

    For advice, if the housing association does not employ a specialist adviser in mental health itself, it should be put in touch with either the social services department or another association which has one.

    The specialist adviser should be invited to a predischarge multidisciplinary planning conference, with the patient's consent, and thereafter, without breaking confidentiality, should advise the housing association on the type of accommodation that is suitable and also that which is not.

    Housing associations should be advised to choose housing for prospective tenants which takes into account the vulnerabilities of neighbours and the special characteristics of the patients.

7. The forensic psychiatric services and the local police forces should jointly devise a liaison policy to guide procedure in the investigation of patients who are suspected of serious personal crime. The policy should include a description of what remedies or disciplinary action might be taken where individuals deviate from agreed guidance.

8. Psychiatrists should provide magistrates, safeguarding confidentiality, with information about their patients who have been arrested and who have a history of mentally abnormal offending, to enable the most appropriate remand to be made.

Each of these recommendations is suitable for medical or multiprofessional service audit.

Recommendations: for the attention of those who provide or regulate services for mentally disordered offenders

9. Each body which is concerned with mentally abnormal offenders should, each year, report agreed measures which show the outcome of its decisions to the body to whom it is responsible. Reporting should be automatic, allowing performance to be judged and if necessary corrected, and not left to fortuitous research.

    We believe that such checks on performance should apply to all such bodies without exception and include Mental Health Review Tribunals, the Advisory Committee on Restricted Patients, the decisions made about mentally disordered offenders by the Department of Health and the Home Office, the Special Hospitals Service Authority and Regional Forensic Psychiatric Services.

10. Policies and procedures regulating what happens to mentally abnormal offenders should be reviewed, revised and monitored, that is, subject to automatic audit.

11. All bodies which are involved in making decisions about the discharge or transfer of detained patients but which are not in clinical contact should use figures gained from research and statistics and from predictive techniques to improve the quality of their judgements. These should supplement information gained from clinical sources.

12. All who provide services for mentally disordered offenders should strongly encourage or commission research into the improved classification of personality disorder and methods of predicting dangerousness.

13. The Special Hospitals Service Authority, regional secure units and the Health and Home Office departments should keep trying to find a better consensus with clinicians on the definition of treatability in personality disorder.

14. Much more priority must be given to the development of places for the patients who no longer need special hospital treatment but who are not yet ready for community placement and who need indefinite kindly containment.

15. Arrangements for the transfer of information contained in clinical notes between hospitals should be improved to satisfy the requirements of both transferring and receiving hospitals.

16. Following consultation, the Department of Health should prepare guidance on placing patients who have shown past evidence of dangerous behaviour with housing associations and similar bodies.

17. Regional health authorities should check whether their regional secure units and other forensic services have developed liaison policies with local police forces.

Recommendations: for research and professional organisations
Because of the confusion with words and concepts, it would be extremely helpful for practitioners, managers, and lawyers if the following issues could be addressed by academic departments of psychiatry and clinical psychology and the Royal College of Psychiatrists:

18. Clarification of the term psychopath to make certain that everyone agrees what is being described, especially in court.

19. A descriptive classification of the disorders of personality to allow shared information and understanding of individuals to be passed between clinicians like other classifications in medical practice.

20. A definition of treatability and the development of measures of change in the extent of personality disorder to demonstrate the effectiveness of treatment.

21. The commissioning of further research into techniques of the prediction of dangerousness, especially for lay members who are asked to make judgements about those people who are very difficult to understand.

Independent Inquiry – Kevin Rooney
Andrew Collins (Chair), Dr Oscar Hill and Michael Taylor – North Thames
Regional Health Authority, December 1992
Synopsis
In May 1991 Kevin Rooney, at the age of 28, killed his girlfriend, Grace Quigley.
He was found guilty of manslaughter on the grounds of diminished responsibility
and was detained under Section 37, MHA, 1983 with a restriction order (Section
41). Kevin Rooney had a history of psychiatric illness dating from 1985. He had
been admitted to hospital for treatment on a number of occasions, the most recent
being for two days the week before the stabbing of his girlfriend. On this occasion
he had left hospital against medical advice.

The early picture is one of relapsing mental illness, necessitating frequent hospital
admissions. The uncertain diagnosis of personality disorder and subsequently
recurrent paranoid schizophrenia is further complicated by drug misuse. Despite
concerted attempts to obtain adequate housing for Kevin Rooney by his social
worker, his fragile mental state was further exacerbated by lack of settled accommodation including bouts of sleeping rough. His unwillingness to be maintained on
medication led in part to a rather chaotic lifestyle. He frequently displayed threatening behaviour but was not considered to be a serious risk to others on the grounds
that he did not carry out the threats. In 1990, while he was in hospital, he met Grace
Quigley, a single parent of Ghanaian descent who was also a hospital inpatient.

This inquiry considers the dilemma posed by the Mental Health Act 1983, namely
that it is concerned with powers to detain people for treatment in hospital but does
not cover compulsory measures to treat patients in the community. Kevin
Rooney's illness became well controlled on medication, while he was in hospital.
But once he was discharged he did not comply with the medication prescribed and
so he relapsed. 'There is no power to force a person to take medication even
though the failure is caused by the illness which the medication is designed to
treat' (Rooney, 1992, para. 33).

Recommendations: Rooney Inquiry
1.   The general practitioner should routinely be informed of the following:
   a)   that a patient has been admitted [to hospital];
   b)   that a patient has gone absent without leave;
   c)   that a patient has been discharged [from hospital]; and
   d)   the details of any medication or treatment regime including what (if
        any) medication he is believed to have in his possession.

2.   Social services must play a key part in monitoring, so far as it is possible, those with a diagnosed mental illness who are in the community. The ASW should be involved both at the admission and discharge stages.

3.   We endorse the measures being taken by the health authority.

   a)   Review and revision of the missing patient policy to include advice on contacting GPs.

   b)   Procedures for medical review of week-end admissions will be reconsidered.

   c)   A form will be devised to be filled in by the duty night co-ordinator to give to the day senior nurse identifying any incident and any patients who have gone absent without leave.

   d)   Further training will be given on risk assessment.

   e)   GPs will be informed if patients fail to attend out-patient appointments.

4.   We think it essential that any individual who has to deal with a mentally ill patient should ask himself whether he needs to give any information to any other person or authority. There must be a general awareness of the need to ensure that those who can help the patient know of him and his difficulties.

5.   In the course of the hearing, the question was raised whether the police should inform the doctors of a patient's criminal record. It is obvious that this might be most important in forming a proper decision in relating to risk. We are satisfied that there are valid objections to a routine disclosure of criminal records. But we think that there are circumstances in which such disclosure should be considered. We are thinking in particular of a S136 referral. We would expect the police as a matter of routine to seek details of someone found in the circumstances covered by S136, if only to see whether they were absconders or wanted for any offence anywhere. It seems to us that, if a person's record shows that he has committed offences or contains information which may be relevant to a determination whether he is at risk (eg. offences of violence or where he has in the past been committed to a hospital, perhaps in another part of the country), the police should be prepared to give the relevant information, at least where the doctor asks, perhaps because he has some doubts. We have not asked for police comment on this suggestion, but we feel that, without such information the doctor may sometimes be disabled from making a correct

decision and this may endanger the public. We do not feel we can be more specific than to recommend that consideration be given to defining the circumstances in which such disclosure could or perhaps should be made.

Report of the Inquiry Panel set up by Nottingham Health Authority to investigate the serious untoward incident at the Tudor Rest Home on the night of 3/4 August 1993
Mrs P Turnbull (Chair), Dr O A Oyebode and Mr J Archer – Nottingham Health Authority, November 1993
Synopsis
This report attempts to preserve the anonymity of the offender and victim by referring to them by their initials. On 3 August 1993 Mr DU stabbed two residents at the residential home where he lived. One of the residents, Mr V, died from his injuries. DU had shared a room with Mr V. At the time of the homicide DU was aged 28 and had a long history of mental health problems and offending behaviour. He had been under the care of Nottingham Mental Health Services since 1990. DU had been a resident at the residential home for three months prior to the fatal incident. Before moving to the residential home, DU had spent eight months in a flat but had encountered difficulties with independent living, hence the move. He was subject to the Care Programme Approach, his care being co-ordinated by the Care Manager, who was also his Community Psychiatric Nurse (CPN). The arrangements for discharge and aftercare were considered to be sound although the role of the general practitioner in the care planning was not well defined.

One of the conclusions of the report stated that 'the shared accommodation and age mix of residents [at the residential home] may have heightened the risk of violence by DU' (DU Inquiry, 1993, para. 5.60). A further consideration highlights the limited range of suitable, available accommodation, most of which is provided by the private sector.

Recommendations: DU Inquiry
Care Programme Approach
1.   The Care Programme Approach should be implemented consistently throughout the service to an agreed timescale in line with Department of Health guidelines. The recommendations made by the regional health authority following their monitoring visit of 16 March 1993 should be adopted.

2.   An agreed method of multidisciplinary assessment together with clear guidelines and standardised documentation should be introduced.

3.   A training programme should be constructed and implemented to support these arrangements and to introduce consistency of approach.

4.   A quality assurance strategy to monitor and audit the value of the new arrangements against agreed outcomes should be established. Full advantage should be taken of the investment made by Dr Ferguson to develop a computerised information system.

Residential Home
5.   The matching of an individual to proposed accommodation needs to be prepared more systematically. Whilst taking account of an individual's preference, accommodation should be carefully assessed in terms of the individual's needs as well as the 'care culture' of the establishment, overall competence and experience of staff and staffing levels, the existing mix of residents, and appropriateness of the physical accommodation.

6.   The summary of need form should be completed taking into account the long-term history of the individual and not only the most recent observations.

7.   Staff in community residential accommodation catering for mentally ill people should receive relevant and appropriate information, advice, and training in working with mentally ill people.

General Practitioners
8.   At the time of discharge from hospital or at change of residence, the community psychiatric service should notify the relevant general practitioner as soon as he or she is known.

9.   This notification should include early contact with the general practitioner by the community psychiatric service with regard to diagnosis, treatment programme, and the support to be provided by the community psychiatric service.

10.   General practitioners should familiarise themselves with the patient's previous mental, as well as medical, history.

11.   The general practitioner must be clear where he or she fits into the community care plan, whether he or she will be simply a point of contact in an emergency, whom he or she should contact at the community psychiatric service, or whether the patient's mental illness will be completely managed by community psychiatric staff.

12.   If the general practitioner does provide an initial emergency service or makes any substantial change to the treatment programme, including medication, he must report such actions to the key worker at the earliest opportunity.

13.   General practitioners should not prescribe psychotropic medication by telephone without first reviewing the patient.

14.   A general practice has round the clock responsibility to the practice patients. This responsibility includes provision when the practice doctors are off duty. When all members of a practice are off duty, it is the doctors' responsibility to ensure that an efficient deputising service is available and functioning.

Communications
15.   Clear guidelines should be produced concerning basic information which should be available to home owners/carers.

16.   There should be prompt information available to general practitioners concerning any significant change in patient circumstances. New general practitioners who are awaiting transfer of medical records should receive basic information about the patient from the care manager as soon as ever practicable.

17.   Arrangements should be made for communication of key information to all relevant parties involved in the care programme. The care manager, or another designated person, should be responsible for receiving and disseminating information to the various parties.

18.   The care manager should be aware of the format of record keeping in the home/hostel and have access to records by prior arrangement with the owner/carer. The care manager should agree with the owner/carer how relevant information will be passed on, either orally or by reference to the home's records.

19.   In the care manager's preliminary review of accommodation he or she should seek to ascertain information on the background, age and mix of residents in a home.

20.   The home owner should receive clear guidelines on whom to contact and how to obtain advice and support at all times – particularly out of hours.

The Report of the Inquiry into the Care and Treatment of Christopher Clunis
Jean Ritchie QC, Dr Donald Dick and Richard Lingham – HMSO, February 1994
Synopsis
In December 1992 Christopher Clunis killed Jonathan Zito, a stranger. He was convicted of manslaughter and detained under Section 37, MHA 1983 with a restriction order under Section 41 of the Act. Christopher Clunis was aged 29 at the time he committed this offence and had already been in contact with British mental health and criminal justice services for five years. However, Clunis's psychiatric history pre-dates this. He had been diagnosed as suffering from paranoid schizophrenia in Jamaica in 1986. During the five years from 1987 to 1992 Christopher Clunis was admitted to a number of different hospitals for brief periods of psychiatric treatment on many occasions. On the whole he experienced poor aftercare and was frequently lost to follow-up by the various services involved. He experienced several moves mostly within north and south London usually because accommodation or hospital beds were unavailable where they were needed. This dislocation contributed to Christopher Clunis's mental health problems and exacerbated the fragmentation of services and the general lack of care for him in the community. In addition his episodes of mental illness and assaultive behaviour were treated separately and incidents of violence were minimised so that there was no proper risk assessment, with no long-term planning for his care in the community.

In addition to the recommendations which are listed below, the report concludes that there were important failures in the following respects:

1. to communicate, pass information and liaise between all those who were or should have been concerned with Christopher Clunis's care in the widest sense of that word: consultant psychiatrists and members of the consultant team; nursing staff; general practitioners; community psychiatric nurses; social workers; the police; the Crown Prosecution Service; the Probation Service; hostel staff; people who provided care from the private sector; and Christopher Clunis's family. Without proper communication and liaison, there cannot be effective care either in hospital or in the community.

2. to contact and involve the patient's family and general practitioner in the provision of care.

3. to obtain an accurate history, or to verify it.

4. to consider or assess Christopher Clunis's history of violence and to assess his propensity for violence in the future.

5. to plan, provide or monitor S117 Mental Health Act 1983 aftercare.

6. to manage or oversee provision of health and social services for the patient/client.

7. to provide assertive care when the patient is living in the community and to note and act upon warning signs and symptoms to prevent a relapse.

8. to identify the particular needs of homeless, itinerant, mentally ill patients on discharge from hospital, to keep track of such persons and to provide for their care even when they cross geographical boundaries.

9. to provide qualified social workers, including sufficient numbers of Approved Social Workers, to assess all new referrals, and to provide supervision and leadership.

10. of the police adequately to recognise and deal appropriately with mentally ill people.

11. to conduct an internal inquiry that was fair, objective, and independent.

The following tendencies were noted repeatedly:

12. to overlook or minimise violent incidents.

13. to care and treat the acute episode of illness without also providing long-term care.

14. to allow geographical boundaries to interfere with or curtail proper provision of care.

15. to postpone decisions or action when difficulty was encountered or perhaps because the patient was threatening and intimidating, and possibly because he was big and black.

Recommendations: Clunis Inquiry
S117 Mental Health Act 1983 Aftercare and the Care Programme Approach
1. The aftercare needs of each individual patient must be assessed by health and social services before the patient is discharged into the community. Such assessment must take into account the patient's own wishes and choices.

2.   A plan of care must be formulated for each individual patient, under the direction of the Consultant Psychiatrist under whose care the patient has been admitted.

3.   The plan must be formulated by all those who will afterwards be responsible for providing any part of the aftercare, so that the plan is made by a team of people who work in a variety of different fields. Such a team for convenience is called the multidisciplinary team. The aftercare plan must be recorded in detail and a copy of the plan must be given to the patient and to all those who are to provide care.

4.   The plan of care must fully consider and provide for both the immediate and long-term needs of the patient.

5.   The Consultant Psychiatrist with responsibility for the patient must assess, together with the multidisciplinary team, the risk of the patient harming himself or others.

6.   Members of the multidisciplinary team should be aware that aftercare is not provided by medication alone, although it is obviously a useful part of the armoury. There is always a need to help the patient come to terms with his illness and for the patient to have proper contact with those people who will be providing him with aftercare.

7.   A keyworker must be agreed who will act to co-ordinate the care that has been planned by the multidisciplinary team.

8.   All members of the team should be alerted to signs and symptoms in the patient which may indicate that they are likely to relapse. Such signs and symptoms may be identified by the doctors but may also be recognised by the patient himself or his relatives or friends. Non compliance with medication should be perceived as a significant pointer to a relapse.

9.   The aftercare that is provided must be properly co-ordinated and supervised; it is severely to the patient's detriment if each member of the team acts in isolation. The Consultant Psychiatrist and Care Manager from social services must together be responsible for supervising aftercare.

10.   It is essential that each member of the team who is providing care for the patient responds effectively to signs and symptoms which suggest that the patient is likely to relapse. Help that can be given before a crisis develops is more beneficial to the patient than the care that can be provided once they are in crisis.

11. When the patient moves from the district where he has previously been receiving care, responsibility for his aftercare should be formally transferred to the services responsible for his care in the district to which he moves.

12. Although Health and Social Services often have boundaries and catchment areas which do not overlap, proper co-operation between those who are providing care is likely to resolve any potential problems. Catchment areas should never be allowed to interfere with proper care in the community.

13. It is essential that the aftercare for patients is properly monitored by Health and Social Services.

14. Any area of unmet need which is identified by the multidisciplinary team must be brought to the attention of the managers of the health and social services.

15. A new form should be designed for use in all S117 aftercare cases, similar to other forms which are presently standardised under the Mental Health Act 1983.

16. The form should record details of the plan that have been agreed, and should name the Consultant Psychiatrist, the Care Manager and the keyworker who together are responsible for the supervision and co-ordination of the plan.

17. Details of the signs and symptoms which suggest a likely relapse should be recorded as should details of the steps that the patient would like to be followed in the event of a relapse occurring. An assessment should be made as to whether the patient's propensity for violence presents any risk to his own health or safety or to the protection of the public.

18. Decisions and further plans that are made subsequently at S117 review meetings, should be recorded on the form as should the decision to discharge the patient from S117 aftercare.

19. A nationally based register for patients subject to S117 Mental Health Act 1983 aftercare should be set up, where information which leads to ready identification of the patient would be stored, and which would indicate whence confidential information about the patient could be obtained.

20. The nominated keyworker in S117 aftercare should always be a qualified and experienced Social Worker or Community Psychiatric Nurse.

21.   Every patient, subject to S117 Mental Health Act 1983 aftercare, should have a nominated relative, friend or volunteer to act as his befriender/ advocate, unless the patient expressly states to the contrary.

22.   Statutory Authorities and Voluntary Agencies working in the field of mental health should recruit, train and support members of the public who wish to be S117 befrienders.

23.   A copy of the current aftercare plan should be given to the befriender.

24.   Before a patient who is subject to S117 aftercare moves from the area where he is being cared for, a joint case conference should be held between those who are currently providing his aftercare and those who will be providing his aftercare in the future. Responsibility will remain with the original multidisciplinary team unless and until S117 aftercare is effectively transferred and a new S117 form is completed by the new multidisciplinary team.

25.   S117 forms should be reviewed regularly by the Hospital Managers as defined under the Mental Health Act 1983.

26.   The Mental Health Act Commission should carry out external monitoring of S117 forms on each statutory visit.

Supervised Discharge Orders
27.   A patient who is detained for treatment under the Mental Health Act 1983 may be made the subject of a Supervised Discharge Order.

28.   The Supervised Discharge Order should contain details of a plan of care which the patient and his Responsible Medical Officer have agreed.

29.   If the Responsible Medical Officer considers that the patient has failed to comply with the plan, or that the patient's mental health is deteriorating, the patient may be recalled to hospital.

30.   A Supervised Discharge Order shall be capable of renewal within six months of the Order being made and for 12-month periods thereafter, but only on the same grounds as the original Order was made.

31.   Each renewal will be subject to the Mental Health Act 1983 appeal procedures.

32.   The patient's Responsible Medical Officer, social worker and keyworker should be named in the Order as should the patient's relative or friend.

33.   Supervised Discharge Orders should be lodged with and monitored by the Mental Health Act Commission.

34.   When the patient moves to another area, those who are nominated in the Order should remain responsible for his care unless and until such care is properly transferred under the Order.

Special Supervision Group of Patients Who Need Special Care
35.   Every psychiatric service should identify patients as part of a Special Supervision Group and should provide a Specialist Team to supervise and support the group.

36.   New funding should be provided for that purpose.

37.   A nationally based Supervision Register for the Special Supervision Group should be set up, where information which leads to ready identification of the patient would be stored, and which would indicate from where confidential information about the patient could be obtained.

38.   Every psychiatric service should appoint specialist community psychiatric nurses to the team responsible for the Special Supervision Group whose only job is to supervise a very limited caseload.

39.   Community Psychiatric Nurses should follow patients across health boundary borders until responsibility is formerly transferred to another specialist team.

Confidentiality
40.   The Department of Health should determine, with the help of Directors of Social Services and others, how the confidentiality of mentally ill patients may be properly protected within the Care Programme Approach.

The Assessment of Dangerousness
41.   An accurate record should be made of any incident of violence and the details should be included in the patient's discharge summary.

42.   An assessment of the risk of dangerousness should be included in the discharge summary whenever the patient has acted with violence.

43. Everyone who has contact in his professional or service work with mentally ill people who may pose a risk of violence should have training in the assessment of dangerousness, and understand when to refer the patient for expert guidance.

Social Services Departments

44. More social workers should be recruited where teams are seen to be under strength, in particular if the team is involved with new referrals.

45. Where social services reception and referral systems are manned by unqualified or inexperienced staff, such staff must have ready access to an experienced Approved Social Worker.

46. Unqualified and recently qualified social workers must work under the supervision of a qualified and experienced manager and their work should be reviewed at least once every fortnight by their supervisors.

47. When current cases involve active danger the daily handover and briefing arrangements for staff should ensure that the case continues to receive prompt attention.

48. There should be close contact and liaison between social services departments and local housing agencies.

49. An Approved Social Worker should be available in each social services department to respond to crises and to provide advice. An Approved Social Worker should be contactable throughout the working day, as well as at night and during weekends and public holidays.

50. Medical recommendations leading to detention should be copied for the Approved Social Worker for his records, and a copy of the Application for Admission recommendation should be kept by him. He should also provide a report for the Hospital where the patient is to be detained and retain a copy of it for the social services file on the patient.

Resources

51. An increased number of Medium Secure Unit beds within the South East Thames Regional Health Authority area is urgently needed. Furthermore, urgent consideration should be given as to whether an increased number of such beds should be provided for every inner city area.

52. There is a clear need for the provision of rehabilitation units to be available to Regional Medium Secure Units.

53. An increased number of beds on general psychiatric wards in London is urgently needed. Furthermore, urgent consideration should be given as to whether an increased number of such beds should be provided in every inner city area.

54. There is a clear need for 'haven type' accommodation for those who cannot cope in the community.

55. There is a clear need for a range of supervised accommodation for those who suffer from mental illness, from intensively staffed hostels with a high degree of nursing care, through warden staffed self contained units, to accommodation that is reserved for mentally ill people who can live more or less independently.

56. There is a clear need for an increased number of forensic psychiatrists.

57. Every psychiatric service should include a doctor who has a special interest in Forensic Psychiatry.

Inspection, Monitoring and Audit

58. It is essential that the Department of Health sets up proper procedures for effective monitoring of psychiatric services in the community.

59. The Department of Health should publish the principles which community mental health services for the seriously mentally ill must follow, and declare minimum standards in manpower and facilities for all services to reach. These should be the basis of what the NHS Management Executive requires each Health Authority to commission for its community

60. A duty should be imposed on service providers in their contracts with commissioning authorities to satisfy an external inspecting or accrediting body that they have currently achieved published standards of service and facilities.

61. The Department of Health should institute a system to inspect community mental health services every three years, and to examine the results of health and social services annual joint reviews, so that national standards may be defined, maintained, and improved upon.

62. When an internal inquiry is carried out within a hospital or social services department it is essential that no fewer than two members of the public are included on the panel to ensure that the Inquiry is as independent and objective as possible. Such members of the public should agree not to divulge any confidential information acquired during the Inquiry.

Mental Illness and Offending

63.   The Home Office should publish a Guide to interpretation of the Circular on Provision for Mentally Disordered Offenders (No 66/90), in which clear advice should be given as to when it is appropriate to charge someone who is mentally ill. Such advice should include guidance as to when medical opinion should be obtained, and as to what matters should be taken into consideration, including the potential seriousness of the charge and the public interest.

64.   A medical recommendation obtained by the Police in relation to a mentally disordered offender must be sent to the Crown Prosecution Service with the papers or as soon thereafter as it is received.

65.   The Consultant Psychiatrist who is responsible for the care of a patient, who has been charged with an offence and remanded to hospital custody must consider whether the patient needs to be detained for treatment under the Mental Health Act 1983, irrespective of the outcome of that charge.

The Police

66.   Officers should be given proper training in mental illness. It is vital that such training should include both knowledge about mental illness and experience of those who suffer from mental illness.

67.   S136 Mental Health Act 1983 procedures and documentation should be standardised.

68.   An Officer should be appointed at every Police Station to deal with mental health issues.

69.   The Police should be encouraged to liaise with local community mental health services.

General Practitioners

70.   General practitioners should be informed of all aftercare plans.

71.   General practitioners should always be invited to attend S117 Mental Health Act 1983 aftercare meetings, and aftercare meetings for vulnerable or severely ill patients.

72.   Discharge summaries should be sent to General Practitioners by Facsimile or at the latest by post within five working days of discharge.

73. Before a General Practitioner may remove a patient from his list, whom he believes or suspects suffers from a psychiatric illness, he must obtain advice from the local psychiatric team and follow such advice, and must inform the Family Health Services Authority of his intention to remove the patient from his list, so that the authority can ensure that the patient is registered with a new General Practitioner as soon as possible.

74. A General Practitioner whose patient is on the Supervision Register or the Mental Health Act 1983 Register must not remove the patient from his list without previously informing the patient's Responsible Medical Officer, and ensuring that another General Practitioner has agreed to act as the patient's General Practitioner.

75. The Royal College of Psychiatrists should be asked to design a crisis card for mentally ill people.

Responding to Crises
76. Each psychiatric service should actively recruit medical practitioners to make certain that there are sufficient doctors in their area who are approved under Section 12 of the Mental Health Act 1983 to ensure prompt response to requests for assessment under the Act.

77. Urgent requests should be met within three hours and non-urgent requests within three working days. The performance of these targets must be properly monitored.

Ethnic Minorities
78. Young black males should not be type-cast as suffering from schizophrenia unless the clinical indications warrant it.

79. Clinicians and others who care for black mentally ill people should not be too ready to ascribe odd behaviour to the abuse of drugs.

80. Young black people should be encouraged to become General Practitioners and Psychiatrists so that the medical service is not seen to be dominated by whites or other ethnic groups.

Volunteers and Members of the Public
81. Members of the public should be encouraged to offer their services, to contribute to the quality of life of those who suffer from mental illness.

82. A 24-hour telephone service to a volunteer should be provided.

Inquiry into the Deaths of Jason and Natalia Harry
Jean Gabbott and Dr Oscar Hill – Haringey Child Protection Committee,
September 1994 (Summary Report)
Synopsis
Sharon D who was born in 1969 had two children, Jason Harry and Natalia Harry. On 23 August 1992 Jason who was six and Natalia who was five were found dead at their mother's home. Sharon subsequently stated that she had heard voices telling her to kill the children. The relationship between Sharon and the children's father ended when Natalia was about one year old on account of his violence. Both children were placed on the Child Protection Register in September 1988, but were removed from it in the summer of 1991 because reports were favourable.

At the end of 1991 Sharon was detained briefly in hospital under Section 2 of the Mental Health Act 1983, diagnosed as suffering from a drug-induced psychosis. Not long after she had been discharged (two weeks) the police were called to Sharon's home because she was holding a knife to the children's throats and threatening suicide. Sharon was remanded in custody and the children were placed with their grandmother. In February 1992 Sharon was sectioned under Section 37 of the Mental Health Act and was admitted to hospital for approximately two months. She was discharged to the care of the day hospital but failed to attend regularly. Section 117 aftercare planning recognised this problem and tried to address it. In June 1992 the children were placed on the register and were to remain in the care of their grandmother. Sharon was not seen by social workers from 15 June until after the death of her children on 23 August. The last occasion on which Sharon was seen by health services was 3 July. In the words of the summary report, 'it is regrettable that the monitoring was essentially performed by grandmother rather than the professionals concerned' (Harry, 1994, para. 9.0).

The report comments on the additional complexity of Sharon's treatment and diagnosis arising from her use of cannabis and how this is perceived by the medical profession. Sharon was born in London of West Indian parents. While the report acknowledges the difficulty of diagnosis in Sharon's case it also says, 'there is a view that cannabis use in the black community is excessively blamed by white psychiatrists as a cause of psychotic disturbance' (Harry, 1994, para. 11.6).

Recommendations: Harry Inquiry
Reorganisation of Social Services
1.   When the planning of organisational change is under way, attention should be given to a detailed and critical analysis of the effects of change likely to occur at the interface between the 'old' and the 'new' with particular regard for the needs of children on the child protection register.

2. We recommend that additional resources directed to ensure a smooth handover in such cases are necessary, for example, an increase in front-line staff for the transition period.

The Area Protection Committee

3. That the Police together with Social Services devise a system whereby when the police are called to an address they would know whether the children are on the child protection register. This issue should be taken up on a national basis by the Home Office and Department of Health.

4. Strategies which aim to improve attendance at child protection conferences should continue to be developed, monitored, and regularly reviewed.

5. Consideration should be given to the provision of a handwritten decision sheet prepared at the conference and outlining family composition, those present, decisions and recommendations, and date of next meeting. This would be taken away with participants and distributed to absentees without delay thus assisting the speedy dissemination of information from conferences to all relevant personnel.

6. Adult psychiatrists may be unfamiliar with child protection issues. Guidance on the minimum communication expectations for the psychiatric services when they are treating a patient where there are child protection issues should be formulated.

7. In cases where there is an alleged criminal aspect professionals should read the policy statements which give a first hand account of incidents in which the client has been involved.

Child Protection Conferences

8. The Chair should routinely ask for the children's views on the situation under discussion and be informed of the efforts made to gain their views.

    The child's right to be heard and his or her wishes taken into consideration is a duty laid on the local authority in the Children Act 1989.

9. More attention should be given to listening and talking with children. Working directly with children should be essential training for social workers involved with children and their families.

10. There should be a standard item on all child protection conference agendas to consider issues of race and culture.

11. It should become Social Services procedure that Minority Ethnic Liaison Officers must be formally consulted on all child protection cases where issues of race and culture have been identified as having an impact on effective intervention in a family.

12. In cases where legal action may be required the Chair should ensure that the team manager and social worker involved in the case discuss legal options with a lawyer from the local authority legal section.

Social Services

13. That a system be set up to monitor that child protection review conferences are held at the required intervals as specified in the child protection procedures.

14. There should be a requirement that specific child protection training be undertaken by newly qualified social workers before they assume responsibility for child protection cases.

15. Transfer summaries on child protection cases should provide an overview of the case and be explicit about the work with the family that must proceed without disruption. Negotiation regarding handover arrangements between outgoing and incoming team managers must take place in order to ensure that the primary goal of maintaining adequate protection of the children continues to be met.

Medical

16. When a sectioned patient on trial leave fails to co-operate with a plan of treatment he or she should be reassessed and if necessary recalled to hospital if there is no other way of making a speedy assessment.

17. We would particularly recommend the freeing up of more time of consultant psychiatrists for liaison, community visits and communication with professionals who are unable to attend ward rounds.

18. There should be multiethnic discussions between Health, Social Services, and Police representatives of ethnic minorities and all other parties with an interest looking at issues around the use of cannabis and how those vulnerable to its effects may be protected.

The Report of the Independent Panel of Inquiry examining the case of Michael Buchanan

Christopher Heginbotham (Chair), Dr Robert Hale, Linda Warren, Tom Walsh and Jacqueline Carr – North West London Mental Health NHS Trust, November 1994

Synopsis

Michael Buchanan killed Frederick Graver (a stranger) in September 1992. Later he was found guilty of manslaughter and sentenced to life imprisonment. Michael Buchanan was born in July 1964 to parents of Afro-Caribbean origin. By the time he was 18 months old he was in residential care because his mother had left and his father was unable to look after him. He returned to his father's care when he was about seven but again his father was not able to manage. Michael Buchanan's childhood was characterised by instability and institutionalised care and by the age of 13 he had come to the notice of the criminal justice system because of a series of offences of theft and robbery. He was detained for the first time under the Mental Health Act 1983 in June 1983 at the age of 18, but had a total of 13 admissions between 1983 and 1992. His offending behaviour continued as did his mental health problems.

The diagnosis was one of mental illness and personality disorder further complicated by addiction to cannabis and crack cocaine. A cycle of offending in order to fund his drug habit, which resulted in custodial sentences and admission to psychiatric care, followed by discharge to the community with poor compliance and further relapse, ensued. He was a difficult patient to manage both in hospital and in the community. These difficulties were exacerbated by inadequate aftercare planning and follow-up in the community.

Recommendations: Buchanan Inquiry

Discharge arrangements

1. Meetings to discuss the discharge of patients under Section 117 or via the Care Programme Approach should be attended by representatives of all disciplines involved in the care of the patient. In respect of mentally disordered offenders this should include representatives of the Police and the Probation Service when there has been contact with the patient in the past and social workers and Community Psychiatric Nurses in all cases.

2. The keyworker or a senior nurse on the ward familiar with the patient should always attend the Section 117 meetings.

3. A named worker should be allocated at the meeting to co-ordinate the care of the patient following discharge.

4. The discharge policy for locked wards should be reviewed to ensure that there cannot be a rapid discharge of patients known to be a risk in the community. Placement in an open or rehabilitation ward should be considered. Failing this a period of leave under Section 17 should be used for detained patients.

5. The implications of discharge should be considered at Section 117 meetings, particularly for patients known to be a risk to themselves or others or those with criminal records.

6. The operational policy of the ward should be reviewed to ensure that staff recognise all aspects of patients' conditions rather than addressing only the immediate and obvious signs of illness. This should embrace the broader aspects of the patient's condition over a longer term rather than responding only to the clearly treatable indicators.

7. The forms used for Section 117 planning should be reviewed and expanded to reflect the decisions made, incorporating details of individual responsibilities for those involved in the aftercare and identifying the name of the keyworker.

8. The method of maintaining casenotes on patients should be reviewed, with a view to holding multidisciplinary records which are chronologically ordered to easily reflect the care afforded patients over time.

Post-discharge arrangements
9. After discharge patients should be placed in appropriate supportive accommodation, staffed and resourced to deal with the patients' needs and behaviour.

10. Trusts should work with purchasing authorities to ensure that there is no contractual disincentive to discharge patients from CPN caseloads whilst they remain ill and a danger to themselves or others.

11. The caseloads of CPNs should be reviewed to ensure that they reflect a reasonable level of workload. CPN caseloads should be reported to management at regular intervals for monitoring purposes.

12. Guidelines should be produced for CPNs explaining the circumstances when a patient who declines a service or goes missing can be discharged from their caseloads.

13. CPNs should not be able to discharge former inpatients from caseloads without gaining the prior agreement of the responsible medical officer or nurse manager.

14. For patients known to be a risk to themselves or others, or likely to break down in the community, a policy should be developed for dealing with them should they fail to maintain contact with their CPN.

15. Consideration should be given to the establishment of a Supervision Register team. It should be dedicated to provide support and an out-reach service to people on the Register, particularly mentally disordered offenders.

Multidisciplinary working

16. Members of the multidisciplinary team should be appropriately trained and experienced to deal with the client group involved.

17. The multidisciplinary working relationship between members of the team should be reviewed, particularly in respect to social work input.

18. Multidisciplinary involvement in discharge planning should be extended to the police and Probation Service where there is a likelihood of reoffending.

19. Social services departments should be asked to give careful consideration to the deployment, training and support of social workers and ensure that the most able and experienced staff are allocated to difficult and demanding patients such as Michael Buchanan.

Department of Health and Home Office

20. An enhanced hospital order should be considered during future discussions on amendments to the Mental Health Act 1983. Such an order would allow longer term involuntary commitment of a patient under tightly defined criteria for treatable personality disorders. Although there is considerable disagreement about the treatability of such disorders, the Panel accept the view given by Dr Nigel Eastman that a spectrum of such disorders exists from those which are wholly untreatable to those which are amenable to appropriate (probably psychological or psycho-therapeutic) treatments. Usually, treatment must take place in a secure setting where patients can feel a degree of safety, and which may take some years. Such an enhanced hospital order would require very careful drafting and controls including:

- that such an order would only be used after other approaches to care had failed;

- that a second specialist opinion was obtained on admission and subsequently at six-month intervals;

- that the patient would have the right to a mental health tribunal hearing to review the detention at regular intervals (normally six monthly);

- that a multidisciplinary review of the effectiveness of treatment be carried out at least annually.

It is suggested that such an order should encourage professional staff to consider offering treatment for periods of two or three years in the first instance subject to the criteria set out above.

21. The availability of medium-secure accommodation should be extended for patients with the mixture of mental disorder exemplified by Michael Buchanan. This recommendation is related to the recommendation on enhanced hospital orders. At present the special hospitals and regional secure units are highly reluctant to take patients with a diagnosis of personality disorder even with some form of overlaid but readily treatable psychotic component. Yet it is only by the availability of such long- term safe environments that patients such as Michael Buchanan will be able to settle to therapeutic regimes, including a range of psychological therapies, which will enable them to overcome the problems which 'created' the personality disorders in the first place. It is recognised that great care must be taken in deciding whether patients would require such long-term secure provision. Tight criteria would be required with very careful assessment and diagnosis. At present, however, significant barriers exist to providing patients such as Michael Buchanan with appropriate special hospital provision. This seems wholly unacceptable given public concerns.

22. Guidance to health authorities and mental health providers should be developed on the appropriate use of Section 37 and its value in providing medium term treatment for people with personality disorders, especially those who have a treatable mental illness component to their disorder.

23. A system for assessing mentally ill offenders over a long term period taking account of their criminal records and mental state assessments should be developed. Where a pattern of repeated episodes of criminal activity linked to mental illness is apparent, assessment for detention under a longer term order, as recommended above, should be undertaken.

24. The resources necessary for the effective implementation of the Supervision Register and where necessary increasing such resources to reflect the demands of inner city levels of psychiatric morbidity should be made available. This should be reconsidered urgently if it is to be effective.

25. Statutory involvement of the Probation Service with mentally ill offenders should be at the discretion of the courts where there is a need for such contact rather than being dependent on the sentences given.

26. Prison Medical Officers should receive training in the psychiatric treatment of mentally ill offenders and be involved in their pre-discharge planning.

27. Patients with a mental illness detained in prison should have the right to regular consultation with a qualified psychiatrist.

Michael Buchanan

28. The final recommendation of this inquiry concluded that Michael Buchanan should be reassessed urgently for a place in a special hospital. It was argued that his mental condition cannot receive the treatment required in the non-therapeutic environment of a maximum security prison and that his eventual release could represent a clear risk to the community.

The Falling Shadow: One Patient's Mental Health Care 1978-1993
Louis Blom-Cooper QC, Helen Hally and Elaine Murphy – Duckworth, January 1995 – Report of the Committee of Inquiry into the events leading up to and surrounding the fatal incident at the Edith Morgan Centre, Torbay, on 1 September 1993
Synopsis
Andrew Robinson killed Georgina Robinson (no relation) on 1 September 1993. He later pleaded guilty to manslaughter and was detained under a Hospital Order with Restriction Order (Sections 37/41) of the Mental Health Act 1983. Georgina Robinson was an occupational therapist working in the same hospital in which Andrew Robinson was a patient. Although this inquiry is usually included in the so-called community care tragedies, Andrew Robinson was in fact an inpatient at the time of the offence. He had, however, been treated within community settings previously. Andrew Robinson was born in 1957 and was 35 at the time he committed the homicide. In 1978 he had committed a very serious offence, threatening a girl, with whom he was infatuated, with a loaded shotgun. As a result of this offence, his developing psychiatric disorder was diagnosed as schizophrenia and he was detained in Broadmoor hospital until 1981 when he was transferred to a local psychiatric hospital. He was conditionally discharged in 1983.

During the course of the next 10 years Andrew Robinson continued to receive psychiatric care both in and out of hospital including a Guardianship Order from 1989 until 1992. After the Guardianship Order was removed Andrew Robinson's mental health again relapsed, without the structure of the good community support of a multidisciplinary team and without regular depot medication. As a result he was readmitted to hospital in June 1993, where he was detained on a Section 4, which, when he was reassessed later, was converted to a Section 3. He was able to leave hospital unauthorised, and on one of these occasions bought a kitchen knife with which he later stabbed Georgina Robinson.

Included in the report is a detailed examination of the basis for thorough risk assessment and management as well as the merits of guardianship. Blom-Cooper emphasises the importance of multidisciplinary teamwork, comprehensive planning, and communication. He highlights many disquieting features of Andrew Robinson's care during the 15 years of his illness until 1993. One of the criticisms of professionals involved is that they did not include Andrew Robinson's parents in a therapeutic alliance and tended to disregard the concern that was repeatedly expressed by them about their son's deteriorating mental health, need for medication and indeed hospitalisation, as well as his level of risk. Another major concern expressed within this report is the fact that, over time, the seriousness of the 1978 offence with the shotgun was minimised.

Recommendations: Robinson Inquiry

1. Mental health units should develop a clear policy on when a personal search will be carried out.

2. It is essential that patients, who are as much at risk of violent incidents as members of staff, should have ready access to incident alarms.

3. It is the primary task of management to ensure that practitioners [in mental health] are adequately versed in the law and practice in mental health and, further, that policies and procedure are properly formulated to instruct and guide all practitioners.

4. It is essential that investigation of the death of a patient should always be conducted with expedition.

5. All notes, medical and nursing, should be amalgamated.

6. Attention should also be paid to integrating hospital and community records. The ideal to aim for is a single mental health record for all patients, irrespective of where they are treated, or by whom.

7. A protocol for granting leave should be drawn up for each patient and, wherever possible, with the full involvement of the patient. The RMO has the ultimate responsibility for the detail contained within that protocol.

8. In order to develop an accurate risk assessment, an index of essential documentation should be developed to serve as a check-list for newly referred patients.

9. Training initiatives aimed at developing clinical supervision skills in senior clinical nurses should be devised. Also, newly qualified nurses and nursing students should receive preparation in what to expect from clinical supervision. Furthermore the principle of clinical supervision should be extended to all mental health professionals at all grades.

10. The trust should develop a clear policy about the values, principles and practices that govern relationships between staff and patients' close relatives, recognising relatives' rights to information, practical assistance and involvement in care and treatment plans; and their need for emotional support and help. The key task in working with relatives is to *engage* them in the overall care plan so that they become partners with the clinical team in their relative's care.

11. Professionals need to be trained to trust the experienced judgement of close family, rather than rely on their own impressions made at one isolated assessment.

12. Members of the public who become victims [of delusional obsessions] should also be heard. The keyworker, the responsible CPN or team social worker, would be ideally placed to make a visit to a member of the public in this situation. No breach of confidentiality will normally be involved in receiving and assessing information but, if there is a clear risk to a member of the public, then there is an overriding duty to breach confidence and to provide information in so far as it is necessary in the interests of a potential victim.

13. For patients not on restriction orders, but for whom medication is essential to control their illness, the clinical relationship must necessarily accommodate pre-emptive action when the patient becomes non-compliant.

14. There is no legal need to await significant deterioration [in a patient's mental health] in order to meet the criteria for compulsory admission.

15. All mental health services should now have a risk management policy.

16. Assessment of risk needs to be a continuing process in which the multi-disciplinary team is repeatedly reappraising a patient's risk of violence to others as the day-to-day circumstances of the patient's life unfold. Such a process is important for both inpatient and community settings.

17. When a patient is referred for the first time, or transferred from another team, there should always be a new clinical assessment, which should include an appraisal of risk of violence.

18. Clinical assessment should *always* include a direct search for thoughts about harming others.

19. There are two types of apparently minor incident to which professional staff should be especially alert, since both may indicate an increased risk of serious assault. The first is one which could have been life-threatening but did not result in injury for example, when an assailant is disarmed before major harm occurs. The second is a series of repetitive minor assaults which are escalating in seriousness.

20. It is insufficient to rely on discharge summaries. With current technology it should be straightforward in complex cases to have a thorough case summary which is updated as new information becomes available. The extended summary should be passed on to future clinical teams. In particular, for patients who have committed grave offences, details of the offence should be passed on to future clinical teams.

21. Teams with the responsibility for managing a patient's risk must be sufficiently in touch with the patient and his or her carers to be aware of, and respond to, circumstances which increase risk of violence.

22. Information about carers' fears of an increasing risk of violence always need to be taken seriously. There is a major administrative task in ensuring that systems are in place which are fail safe against human forgetfulness and work overload. When there is a high risk to members of the public, or family, or other carers, there will be some occasions when confidential information must be revealed to carers or to the police.

Independent Panel of Inquiry into the Circumstances Surrounding the Deaths of Ellen and Alan Boland
Mrs J Hughes (Chair), Mrs L Mason, Dr R Pinto and Mr P Williams – Report to the City of Westminster, the Kensington & Chelsea and Westminster Health Authorities and the North West London Mental Health NHS Trust March 1995

Synopsis

In March 1994 Alan Boland killed his mother, Ellen Boland, with whom he lived. He was charged with her murder and remanded in prison. While on remand in May he cut his wrists and was transferred to the hospital wing but was found dead in his cell in July 1994, having hanged himself. Alan Boland was aged 44 when he and his mother died. For the previous nine years Alan Boland had received out-patient psychiatric treatment, having been referred by his GP, and had also attended the day hospital since 1993. The report states that the only detailed case history was taken two weeks after this first referral. The information it contained included *inter alia* that ' "there was obviously a lot of psychopathology" in the relationship with his mother dating from early childhood' (Boland, 1995, para. 26). Two months before his mother died it is recorded that Alan Boland was illegitimate and this had been a secret within the family.

Alongside Alan Boland's mental health problems of anxiety and depression superimposed on a paranoid personality, he was convicted in 1986 of armed robbery and in 1989 was placed on probation for assault and robbery. He was also admitted to hospital on one occasion in 1986 for detoxification. During his nine years of regular outpatient appointments (which he attended) he was seen by a series of 20 junior doctors. There was very little contact or communication with other agencies, despite acknowledgement of Alan Boland's need for re- housing independently of his mother. For example there was no contact between the medical team and the probation service during the course of Alan Boland's probation order. There was no multidisciplinary team approach to, and no real planning for, his care.

Recommendations: Boland Inquiry

1. The relevant NHS Trust should ensure that all new patients referred to the Outpatients Clinic are seen by or discussed with the Consultant or Senior Registrar and that the resulting formulation is clearly recorded in the casenotes and communicated to the General Practitioner.

2. The Trust should ensure that it becomes standard procedure for outpatients carried by a junior doctor to be discussed with the Consultant when the junior doctor comes to the end of his or her placement with the team. A review and possible reformulation of the patient's problems should be recorded in the casenotes. At the least, a handover note should be made in the casenotes describing the salient problems for the junior doctor who next takes over the case.

3.   The Trust should ensure that, as part of the care plan, there are regular reviews of the progress of patients attending the Outpatients Clinic by senior doctors, if possible with other members of the multidisciplinary team, so that social and psychological dimensions can be identified and dealt with.

4.   The Trust should consider inviting relatives or friends to the initial appointment and to subsequent reviews so that a fuller picture of the patient's back ground can be obtained.

5.   The Trust should ensure that, where it is suspected that a social problem is significantly contributing to a patient's illness, the aetiology is pursued either by referral to the Social Services Department or by establishing family work within the Outpatients Clinic. Thus, if a patient fails to

respond to a particular line of care, other dimensions of the case – including psychosocial dimensions – can be considered and explored with members of the multidisciplinary team.

6.   The Trust should clarify roles and responsibilities of the junior doctors, the consultant and the senior registrar in relation to the Day Hospital. The clarification should be incorporated into the operational policy of the Day Hospital.

7.   The Trust should consolidate and amalgamate the various sources of information, particularly separate sets of casenotes, about patients attending different facilities.

8.   The Trust should urgently reappraise the roles of different staff members in relation to the discharge process. It may be appropriate for the keyworker to co-ordinate and communicate the fact of discharge to the General Practitioner but this should be followed by a more detailed letter from the medical staff which should include a review of progress and the keyworker's impressions of the case.

9.   The Trust must ensure that a policy is established and procedures written down so that the Care Programme Approach is implemented in respect of discharges from the Day Hospital, as well as in-patient care, as required by the NHS and Community Care Act 1990 (HC(90)23).

10.   The Health Authority will need to monitor the application of the Care Programme Approach by the Trust and report progress to members at regular intervals in accordance with Health Service Guidelines (94)27.

The story of Ellen and Alan Boland largely preceded these guidelines. But it illustrates some of the dangers that may lie ahead as purchasers set about 'ensuring, through these arrangements, that the necessary priority is given to the most severely mentally ill patients'.

11. The Trust and the Health Authority should review the provision of community psychiatric nurses and, with Recommendations 9 and 10 in mind, address any under-resourcing.

12. The Trust should ensure that the channels of communication between the medical teams and the Social Services Department are kept in good repair although there is no longer a social work attachment to medical teams. Whatever the details of delivery, they should be such that any client can be assessed by a social work care manager and appropriate arrangements made for them, post-assessment (see Recommendation 17 below).

13. The Trust should establish guidelines for offering assistance to the police or Prison Service when a known patient is held in custody. These will need to address the issue of when and in what circumstances the professional duty of patient confidentiality should be overridden. (The Trust may wish to refer, among other sources, to the Report of the Committee of Inquiry into the fatal incident at the Edith Morgan Centre, [Blom-Cooper, 1995].)

14. The Trust should ensure that, if patients are kept on in the Outpatients Clinic primarily for the purpose of being recruited into a drug trial, the proposition should be discussed and agreed with the patient, the patient's General Practitioner and the local ethical committee.

15. The Trust should ensure that there are formal procedures for debriefing staff in the event of a serious incident, whether the incident involves a current inpatient, outpatient or day patient or someone who has recently been discharged from inpatient, outpatient, or day care.

16. The Trust should ensure that a review takes place to establish a standard procedure for recording important messages received, eg. by daily log.

17. The Social Services Department and the Health Authority should review the allocation of resources and their systems so as to ensure that people who present apparently mild or moderate mental health problems can be helped to access appropriate services (see Recommendations 10 and 12 above). This review should include exploring the extent to which voluntary organisations can be more effectively involved.

18.   The Social Services Department should articulate guidelines for the deployment of 'appropriate adults'. It is the opinion of the Inquiry that a social worker should carry out the role of 'appropriate adult'. The Inquiry further recommends that a full report is made on each occasion when a social worker acts as an appropriate adult.

19.   The Social Services Department should review their procedures for recording information about people with whom they have been involved. While there is in existence a system for recording assessments and ongoing contacts, there seems to be no adequate retrieval system for recording requests for information by outside organisations or for recording how such requests are relayed or actioned.

20.   The Housing Department and its Medical Adviser, together with the Medical Practitioners and the Health Authorities, should establish a formal mechanism through which they develop and keep under review the medical criteria and the application procedures for obtaining priority housing on medical grounds.

21.   Such criteria and procedures should accommodate the difficulties liable to arise with applications for housing priority which may be based on psychiatric, as opposed to physical, disorders.

22.   The criteria and procedures, together with the limitations on the total number of lettings available for applications made on medical grounds, should be publicised locally.

23.   The Housing Department should improve the scope and the quality of the advice it provides to housing officers on how to implement its policies and procedures.

24.   The Housing Department should examine the nature and occasion of the guidance given by senior managers to junior housing officers in cases of particular complexity.

25.   The Housing Department should, as part of service development, examine its procedures, publications, standard letters and other communications, internal and external, to ensure that they are clear, comprehensive and comprehensible.

**Report of the Inquiry into the circumstances leading to the death of
Jonathan Newby (a volunteer worker) on 9 October 1993 in Oxford**
*Nicola Davies QC (Chair), Richard Lingham, Clifford Prior and Professor
Andrew Sims – Oxfordshire Health Authority, July 1995*
Synopsis
Jonathan Newby was a young volunteer worker at a Cyrenian hostel in Oxford.
He was untrained and on the week-end of his death was working alone in the
hostel. In October 1993 one of the hostel residents, John Rous, stabbed Jonathan
Newby and killed him. (This report is unusual in that it is named after the victim
and not the offender.) John Rous pleaded guilty to manslaughter and was placed
on a Hospital Order with a Restriction Order (Section 37/41) of the MHA 1983.

John Rous was born in June 1946 and although the detail of his early life is
unclear, he spent the latter part of his childhood in foster care. He had a long
history of mental health problems and offending behaviour, having first come to
the attention of the criminal justice system at the age of 17. A year later he was
admitted to psychiatric hospital for the first time. During the next 30 years John
Rous's mental health history continued with a diagnosis changing from personality disorder to schizophrenia. He also had a serious problem of drug and alcohol
dependency. John Rous's problems had for many years been compounded by a
lack of stable accommodation with the necessary level of support, culminating in
his residency at a Cyrenian hostel. However, his long-standing problems were
such that he probably needed specialised care which was unavailable to him.
Despite his complex needs for an integrated care package, John Rous received his
support largely from voluntary agencies. For many years he had found temporary
accommodation in a series of night shelters, squats, and bed-and-breakfast accommodation, apart from a three-year period in a rented flat. Support from his
probation officer was forthcoming while he was subject to probation orders, and
he received intermittent social work help. Throughout, he maintained contact
with his general practitioners, their practice nurse, and his psychiatrist.

Recommendations: Newby Report
Joint Liaison between Social Services and the NHS
1.   The NHS commissioning authority and Department of Social Services should
       make a joint plan which is then carried out to make provision for all severely
       mentally ill people living in their area. This should include provision for the
       homeless severely mentally ill for whom the high concentration of skills and
       professional training of the health provider Trust are particularly required.
       Access to services for the mentally ill, both within and outside normal
       working hours, for both routine and emergency care, should be advertised to
       users, carers, other statutory bodies, and voluntary agencies.

Social Services

2.   Departments of Social Services have both statutory and moral responsibilities to those requiring community care for mental illness who are receiving services from voluntary organisations. Terms of contracts with these organisations should be defined so that standards relate to those of statutory health and social services and the standards should be reviewed systematically on a case review basis. Means of access to the advice and experience of Approved Social Workers should be defined and availability made public for the benefit of clients' carers and agencies providing care.

Training

3.   Any establishment providing full-time and permanent care for severely mentally ill people will require the services and expertise of trained mental health professionals. Responsibility for this provision and for its specification lies with both the managers of the establishment and the registration authority. In addition all employees require a programme of in-service training.

3.1.   The programme of in-service training for employed staff and for volunteers should be intensified and be better directed to the needs of the severely mentally ill and the staff caring for them. To be more specific, without implying their relative importance or the amount of time that should be spent on each, the following should be considered:

i)   the signs and symptoms of major mental illness

ii)   understanding and learning to talk with severely mentally ill people

iii)   substance abuse and its management: alcohol and drugs

iv)   treatment and management of mental illness: physical, psychological and social

v)   Mental Health Act and its application

vi   Care Programme Approach: Supervision Registers: power of supervised discharge

vii)   risk assessment

viii)   emergency assessment and admission procedures

ix)   record keeping.

3.2   These topics should be in addition to those, such as coping with violent episodes, which are already covered. There are undoubtedly members of staff of the statutory authorities who could teach and conduct seminars on the above subjects. It would be a valuable exercise in tripartite co-operation (voluntary agencies, social services, and health) to organise and carry out such a programme. The staffing, funding, and organisation of work of the statutory authorities should allow for such teaching and discussion to be seen as an essential activity directed towards improving the health of the people.

3.3   There should be developed an NVQ or similar qualification to provide a 'core competence' for those working with the severely mentally ill in the community.

3.4   In addition to providing a core competence, there should be a second accredited level for those operating as keyworkers.

Registration
4.   The registration authority (Department of Social Services) through its duly authorised arrangements for inspection (Social Services Inspectorate) should specify clearly and unequivocally the standards required for each individual residential home (whether it be a part of a larger organisation or not) in terms of buildings and their layout, amenities and equipment; type of resident and their number; number of staff on duty at any time, their experience and professional qualifications; in-service training needs. The authority has a duty to ensure that these specifications are both fully understood and comprehensively complied with. Every visit of the registration authority to the residential establishment should be recorded.

The Registered Homes Act 1984
5.   The Department of Health should review its guidance to Local Authorities having responsibilities under the Registered Homes Act 1984 to ensure that:

i)   The regulations should require the production of staff rotas to registration and inspection staff.

ii)   The regulations should require inspectors to check that the Care Programme Approach has been considered by registered homes.

iii)   The advice about staffing levels should be clarified to remove any ambiguities.

Emergency Procedures

6.   The Health Authority and Social Services Authority should ensure that all such service providers are aware of the steps to be taken and the persons to contact in the event that an emergency assessment or admission to hospital appears necessary for a client. This information should be published and made widely available throughout the field of statutory and voluntary care, to carers themselves, and to other agencies such as police and emergency services.

Police

7.   When a person taken into police custody for a serious crime can reasonably be suspected of significant recent use of alcohol or non-prescribed drugs a police surgeon should be summoned rapidly so that appropriate testing can be carried out, subject to the consent of the suspect.

7.1   The police should keep a log of all telephone calls which have been 'cut-off', accidentally or deliberately.

7.2   The police should ensure that police switchboard operators inform the radio operator of all calls which have been deliberately terminated.

Housing

8.   The Housing Department should, for all cases coming to their attention of people who are both homeless and severely mentally ill, consult with, take advice from, and collaborate with the appropriate Social Services Department. Decisions regarding placement should be made jointly taking into account the opinion of the keyworker. There is a need for exchange of information and provision of expert advice between Social Services Departments, statutory mental health providers, and the Housing Department.

8.1   Homeless people assessed as vulnerable by reason of mental illness should automatically be referred for assessment by social services unless this has already been carried out. The Department of the Environment should include this requirement in guidance to homeless persons units.

8.2   Housing should always be regarded as an integral part of a care plan by key-workers and care managers.

8.3   Providers of housing with care should take all reasonable steps to identify the needs of people referred to them, and satisfy themselves that they can meet these needs. They should ensure that their referral forms ask direct questions regarding all their criteria for acceptance and for exclusion. They should ask these questions of the individual referred and of all the care agencies involved: crucial information may only be known to one agency.

8.4 Housing associations and voluntary agencies providing housing with care should take all reasonable steps to meet the professional standards of care required by their residents. Such agencies should recognise that thy are no longer meeting the needs of people who fall outside the mainstream of community care: they are providing the mainstream of community care.

8.5 The Departments of Health and the Environment should clarify their responsibilities for funding housing for people with severe mental illness, and ensure that their funding arrangements are fully complementary. Adequate funds should be made available to house and provide care for all those with severe mental illness, including street homeless people, those with multiple problems, and those needing continuing long term care.

Committees of charitable organisations

9. Committees of charitable organisations should be, and should be seen to be, independent of their employed officers and staff. New members of the committee and the committee chairman should be selected by existing committee members. It should be recognised that committee membership confers management responsibilities. There should be regular communication between committee members and senior members of staff as well as the chief officer. Members of the committee have a statutory obligation to visit the organisation and a moral obligation to spend time there and to get to know staff and residents.

9.1 Committees should never let one person become their sole source of information about the state of affairs in the charity's work. There should always be regular personal contact between a number of committee members (not just the chair) and a number of senior staff, in an organisation of any size. No other approach is as effective as such personal contacts.

9.2 Management information should be required on all the main aspects of the charity's work. In the case of the Cyrenians, housing management, care services, staffing matters and complaints should have been monitored along with developments and finance. Committees should not be deterred from questioning either the figures presented or why other information has not been presented.

9.3   Committee representatives should be involved in the recruitment of the next
        tier of managers below the chief officer. Such posts should be openly
        advertised.

9.4   Committee members should regularly and actively monitor the quality of
        services actually being provided, either seeing it themselves first hand or
        obtaining independent reports.

9.5   Employees should be able to make direct representations to committee
        officers or members where line management fails to communicate legiti-
        mate complaints regarding the care of clients and the management of
        services. The Nolan Committee's suggestion that public bodies should
        designate an official or board member to investigate staff concerns may well
        be equally relevant to the charity sector.

Central government and the Department of Health
10.   Community care for the mentally ill and contributions towards that care
        coming from the voluntary sector ('the mixed economy') are both frequently
        expressed policies of the Government via the Department of Health.
        Government should specify standards of care and levels of professional
        qualifications and in-service training required by employed staff for the care
        of severely mentally ill people in the community and ensure that the
        resources are available to meet these standards.

10.1   There is a real sense, communicated by staff of voluntary and statutory
        organisations and friends and relations of Jonathan Newby alike, that the
        loose structures of inadequate integration of separate services and meagre
        distribution of professional expertise appeared to have been sanctioned by
        Government in carrying out a new policy without adequate preparation and
        resourcing.

10.2   The voluntary agencies, especially the Cyrenians, attempted to fill a gap in
        the provision of services – residential care for the homeless mentally ill.
        The Social Services Department of Oxfordshire County Council had not
        been involved either with the identifying of or providing for this deficiency
        in as much as the responsibility for finding accommodation for homeless
        mentally ill people had fallen on the Housing Department of the City of
        Oxford, a separate authority. Whereas the Health Authority would have
        provided comprehensive care for psychiatric inpatients, it would only give
        intermittent outpatient care via a consultant psychiatrist to a person whose
        key-worker came from an independent voluntary organisation and whose

accommodation was provided by another voluntary agency. There is clearly a need for much better organisation and integration for care of individuals with severe mental illness. This might be achieved by clarifying the role and responsibilities of the Responsible Medical Officer in the community and ensuring that the resources including relevant trained personnel were available to do this.

Confidentiality
11. The Department of Health should complete its review of confidentiality and information exchange between the various agencies involved in community care for people with mental illness, and disseminate clear guidelines widely.

Report of the Inquiry into the Care and Treatment of Philip McFadden
Dr James Dyer (Chair), Dr Elizabeth McCall-Smith, John Sutherland and Jamie Malcolm – Mental Welfare Commission for Scotland, August 1995
Synopsis
In June 1994 Philip McFadden stabbed and killed a young police constable, Lewis Fulton. At Edinburgh High Court Philip McFadden was found insane in bar of trial and was detained in hospital under Section 174 of the Criminal Procedure (Scotland) Act 1975.

Philip McFadden was born in October 1975 and for most of his life lived in Glasgow. His father was away much of the time working on oil rigs and his parents separated when he was about 12. He had little contact with his father after that time. By 1990, when Philip McFadden was 14, he came to the notice of the Children's Panel because of truanting and vandalism. He also began to show signs of mental illness in 1990 and was admitted to an inpatient adolescent unit in 1991 when, after a period of assessment, a diagnosis of schizophrenia was made. Two months after his discharge from the inpatient unit his brother was killed by a train. After his discharge Philip McFadden became a day patient although his attendance was erratic. Later he was offered outpatient appointments. Medication and psychiatric contact were maintained until July 1993. At the end of 1993 Philip McFadden was transferred from the adolescent psychiatric services to adult services. Throughout his contact with adolescent services, Philip McFadden's care was well co-ordinated and the service he received was good, with considerable effort being made to keep him in contact. The family was also well supported by a nurse practitioner at the GP surgery.

Philip McFadden's mental state deteriorated when he stopped taking medication and he refused adult psychiatric services. Immediately before he committed the index offence, Mrs McFadden tried to obtain help for her son because he had a knife and she perceived there to be an immediate risk of violence. The GP surgery was contacted but the GP on call did not know Philip McFadden well and was unwilling to go to the house because McFadden was armed. One of the contentious issues addressed by this report is the responsibility a GP has towards a mentally ill patient who may pose a risk of violence. After the GP decided not to assess his patient the police were called to the house. One policeman was killed and the other injured. The report concludes that the GP 'too readily decided that it was a police matter and not a medical matter' (McFadden, 1995, p.18).

Recommendations: McFadden Report
With more people with mental illness being treated in the community rather than in hospital, both general practitioners and the police are going to have more contact with them and responsibilities to them. The degree to which the training of both is orientated towards mental health issues needs to reflect this. We are aware that the Scottish Office is currently conducting a review of guidelines for interviewing of mentally disordered people by the police, and welcome this, but the wider training issue is also relevant. Although dealing with a patient with schizophrenia is an infrequent event for a GP and dealing with a violent psychotic patient is an even more infrequent one, GPs need to feel comfortably equipped to cope with such situations. There is also a need for appropriate liaison arrangements between health services, social workers, and police which can be brought to bear in emergency situations, rather than each one having to be worked out at the time.

While attention has, understandably, been given to the growing problem of threats of premeditated violence to GPs going about their business, this has perhaps overshadowed the issue of violence arising from acute psychiatric illness. It may well be that further guidance needs to be addressed to this question in order to help general practitioners. We have also been reminded of the need for clarity of the borderline of responsibility between primary and secondary care. General principles need to be given concrete reality which is understood by everyone involved in local situations.

1. We recommend that the Secretary of State and the Royal College of General Practitioners and other appropriate GP organisations consider the need for further guidance for GPs in dealing with potentially violent mentally disturbed patients in community care.

2. We think there may be value in further discussions at a national level between police and GP representatives in order to address the issue of collaboration in respect of crisis situations involving people with mental

illness who are potentially violent. Arrangements also require to be agreed in local areas between GPs, psychiatric services, mental health officers, and the police with reference to collaborating over such emergency situations.

3.   As a general issue, the development of community care requires that the training of the police be appraised to ensure that there is adequate preparation for recognising mental illness and dealing with members of the public who are mentally ill.

These recommendations are made in order to assist future practice. They arise from the inquiry team's discussions surrounding Philip McFadden's story and not necessarily precisely from that story itself.

The Woodley Team Report – Report of the Independent Review Panel to East London and The City Health Authority and Newham Council, following a homicide in July 1994 by a person suffering with a severe mental illness
Len Woodley QC (Chair), Ken Dixon, Vivien Lindow, Oyedeji Oyebode, Tom Sandford and Stephen Simblet – East London & The City Health Authority and Newham Council, September 1995
Synopsis
In July 1994 SL killed BB. Both men were mental health service users attending the same social services day centre, where the homicide occurred. SL pleaded guilty to manslaughter on grounds of diminished responsibility and was detained in hospital under a hospital order with a restriction order (Section 37/41 MHA 1983).

SL's mother had a long standing severe mental illness and the family were known to health and social services agencies all of SL's life. SL was born in August 1968 in London, his parents originating from Dominica. He was one of four brothers, his parents separated when he was three, and two of his brothers had been admitted to local authority care for part of their childhood. By the age of 19 SL had sought help from his GP because of panic attacks and a year later he was referred to a psychiatric outpatient clinic where a schizoid personality disorder was diagnosed in addition to severe anxiety and agoraphobic symptoms. By 1990 his lifestyle was becoming disturbed and chaotic, evidenced by problems such as unemployment, accommodation difficulties, and theft. In 1991, at the age of 22, SL was reported to have badly assaulted his mother but charges were never brought. In 1991 SL was convicted of offences of robbery and burglary and received a four-year custodial sentence. A diagnosis of paranoid schizophrenia was made. He was later transferred under Section 47/49 of the Mental Health Act 1983 to a medium secure hospital.

The Woodley Report is unequivocal that SL should have received a hospital order instead of a prison sentence in August 1991 and been diverted from the criminal justice system. The Report considers that this had important consequences for subsequent care and treatment. After assessment at the medium secure unit, SL was transferred to a medium secure hospital in the private sector, some distance from his home area. This created various difficulties particularly regarding planning for his rehabilitation and aftercare. The resulting multidisciplinary approach was fragmented and militated against proper risk assessment. In particular, 'attempts to provide [SL] with good social care were undermined by inadequate health care' (Woodley, 1995, p99). He was discharged from hospital in Cambridgeshire in December 1993 with a Section 117 aftercare plan. Three weeks before he committed the homicide the statutory responsibility to provide aftercare under Section 117 of the Mental Health Act 1983 was discharged by the health and social services authorities involved. This report is extremely thorough and provides a comprehensive overview of a number of issues. For example, it addresses the problem of providing services for children who are being cared for by a mentally ill parent. It is also one of the few reports which considers 'the lack of response to the race and ethnicity dimensions of SL's health care, and the effects of institutional racism' (Woodley, 1995, p3).

Recommendations: Woodley Report
Childhood and Mental Illness: Preventive support network
1.   That the Department of Health give greater emphasis to preventive support work to children with parents with severe mental health problems, and commission and publish research which includes longitudinal studies, cultural variations, and the effect of institutional racism.

Childhood and Mental Illness: Service planning for children and parents
2.   That local social services and health authorities address the support needs of parents with severe mental health problems, and the needs of their children, in community care plans and in children's services plans, and allocate resources. In so doing, that they review the distribution, co-ordination, and access to specialist mental health services for children and families.

3.   That Area Child Protection Committees raise awareness of mental health issues and promote good intra-agency practices.

4.   That the principles expounded in the Leeds Study (Elliott, 1992) be adopted by health, education and social services authorities.

Criminal Justice and Mental Health Needs: Prison service

5. That the prison service should have guidelines for the health care staff about the care of mentally disordered people in prison, particularly with regard to seeking an opinion from the catchment area psychiatrist, rather than transferring inmates from prison to prison, keeping people in minimally furnished cells, or persistently medicating them against their will.

6. That the prison service implements a better administrative procedure for keeping its health care records (as we believe very useful information could be lost with the present system, which has resulted in vital records being misplaced and not traceable: computerisation could be a solution).

Hospital – Assessment, Care and Treatment: Interim Secure Unit

7. In view of the level of disturbance of patients, the nature of their serious offences, and the vulnerability of women as a small minority group in a locked setting within the overall patient population, that a dedicated women-only ward be established within the new purpose-built secure unit currently being commissioned by the local health authority to comply with the Department of Health's Patient s Charter.

8. It appears that the current redevelopment of the Hackney Unit will still leave a significant shortfall in terms of bed numbers and therefore a range of secure provisions should be developed which are closer and more accessible to the London Borough communities from which so many of the current referrals are made.

Hospital – Assessment, Care and Treatment: Commissioning Health Authorities

9. That health authorities which have no alternative but to commission the placement of patients long distances from their homes, make available funds to enable relatives and close friends to visit patients where this is beneficial to their care and rehabilitation.

Hospital – Assessment, Care and Treatment: Kneesworth House Hospital

10. That Kneesworth House Hospital develop and implement more positive action policies for responding to the needs of patients from ethnic minorities and the needs of women patients.

11. That Kneesworth House Hospital continue to develop and implement a strategy for relieving the unacceptably cramped conditions of its ward areas.

12.   That Kneesworth House Hospital review the occupational and educational programmes available to patients in terms of their appropriateness and accessibility to the populations they serve.

13.   That Kneesworth House Hospital develop and implement a strategy which ensures that the clinical teams place more emphasis on therapeutic intervention with patients, including recognition of the need to empower patients by training and providing information about signs and symptoms patients can recognise in themselves.

14.   That Kneesworth House Hospital develop and implement a policy for involving patient advocates. Although we are pleased about revisions that have been made to their complaints procedure since SL's admission, we believe there is still a need for independent advocacy.

15.   That Kneesworth House Hospital ascertain the availability of key personnel from district teams before convening statutory aftercare planning meetings.

Hospital – Assessment, Care and Treatment: Community Services
16.   That district health authorities and local social services authorities make it obligatory for their respective representatives to attend aftercare planning meetings pursuant to their duties under Section 117 of the Mental Health Act 1983 (and in so doing facilitate such attendance).

Hospital – Assessment, Care and Treatment: Local Social Services Authorities
17.   That robust attempts are made to retrieve any existing family or personal history from social services records to facilitate assessment and diagnosis of persons admitted to hospital secure units, and with a view to future social work involvement.

Care in the Community: Housing
18.   That bed and breakfast hotel accommodation should not be used for homeless people with mental health needs.

19.   That where social work or health practitioners make a supporting application for ordinary housing in respect of people recovering from a severe mental illness who have a forensic history of violence, they must disclose this aspect in their report, together with a risk assessment giving explicit reasons why ordinary housing is considered appropriate. The report to the housing agency must identify the Care Programme Approach keyworker or Community Care manager as a contact in the event of concerns.

20. That the service users' permission must be sought for disclosure from health and social services records to housing agencies of information about themselves, and the content of and reasons for disclosure given to them.

21. That housing authorities and housing associations must have a policy on confidentiality which enables transmission of personal confidential information on the basis of 'need to know' for purposes of determining suitable housing allocation, and for the subsequent protection of service users, staff and members of the public.

22. That the service user must be informed of how housing policy on confidentiality will operate. The housing policy must allow for access by service users to their own housing records.

23. That the housing agency must notify the service user's keyworker/care manager of the name of the housing officer who will have most contact with the service user, and of the housing management support role the housing officer performs. Thereafter, the keyworker/care manager must ensure that effective liaison is maintained with the housing officer.

24. That the keyworker/care manager, or housing officer, review with a service user, who is socially isolated, their contact with neighbours. Where it appears that a neighbour has, or would be likely to offer, a befriending role that neighbour should be approached and the identity of the keyworker/care manager or housing officer made known as a contact in the event of concerns about the service user's well-being.

25. That the Department of Health, Department of the Environment, and Housing Corporation make known the above recommendations to the agencies concerned.

Care in the Community: Finance
26. That the Government increase the level of funding to the Social Fund for community care grants in areas of high need for mental health service users.

27. That the Benefits Agency improve its performance in dealing with applications for community care grants (where otherwise delay affects an individual's ability to furnish and equip accommodation following the offer of rehousing, and where such delay incurs additional public expenditure, i.e. housing benefits on two tenancies).

Care in the Community: Employment

28.   That in community care assessments and reviews, greater prominence be given to issues of access and personal support needs of people wishing to re-enter open employment.

Care in the Community: Day care services

29.   That large institutional day centres should be reprovided in local areas.

30.   That assessment of an individual's day care needs should form part of comprehensive assessment (through the care programme approach or care management), and individual care plans devised which tailor services to the needs of individuals. In consequence, the traditional method of referral by day centre application form should be reviewed.

31.   Where the primary benefit to some service users who have a serious and enduring mental illness of using day centre facilities, has been to develop self-confidence and social skills, consideration should be given to promoting user empowerment by encouraging self-management arrange-ments with a lower staffing complement, in premises which reflect ordinary life principles (eg. community centres), and in smaller groups which reflect common interests.

32.   Where the primary benefit of day services to some service users is rehabilita-tive or therapeutic, the skills and experiences of day care support workers should be tailored towards meeting individual rather than group needs, with outreach to enable social integration in the community.

Care in the Community: Health and safety

33.   That local social services and district health authorities review their policies and procedures for risk assessment and risk management, in conjunction with service users, for purposes of the following:

●   internal transmission of confidential personal information between service units on a 'need to know' basis

●   disclosure to external agencies providing community care services on a 'need to know' basis

●   production of a service user consent form

●   inclusion in Health and Safety at Work and 'Violence' Guidelines.

34.   That the Department of Health produce guidance, in consultation with public and voluntary bodies as well as with mental health service user

representatives, on criteria for disclosure of personal confidential information concerning risk of violence where the public safety is the overriding consideration.

35. That the local health authority ensure that health service providers with responsibility for mental health service users who have a forensic history, jointly produce a protocol and criteria concerning follow up arrangements by forensic and general consultant psychiatrists, applicable to the area of residence of the service user and in consultation with local social services authorities.

36. That the Department of Health, health authorities and social services authorities recognise the need for, and facilitate training in, on-going risk assessment and risk management for mental health practitioners in the context of multidisciplinary working arrangements in the community.

Care in the Community: Section 117, Care Programme Approach and Care Management

37. That the Department of Health harmonise guidance on Section 117 Registers, proposed supervision registers, and the care programme approach with community care assessment and care management in respect of people who have a severe mental illness and their carers. Such guidance should include clarification of clinical, management and practitioner responsibilities and the importance of choice by the service user in who their psychiatrist or keyworker is to be for purposes of sustaining a therapeutic relationship.

38. That the Department of Health, in issuing guidance, give recognition to disparities in information technology development throughout the health and social services.

39. That social services and district health authorities jointly assess training needs and develop joint training strategies to promote multidisciplinary working arrangements for Care in the Community, in conjunction with service users and housing and voluntary organisations.

40. That social services and district health authorities promote the involvement of voluntary organisations run by black and other ethnic minority groups in aftercare planning for inpatients from these communities.

41. That the local social services department and health authority review their policy and procedures for the discharge of their duties under Section 117 of the Mental Health Act 1983, and ensure that they have quality assurance

monitoring in place to satisfy themselves that the individuals concerned are no longer in need of such aftercare services.

42. That the local social services department review the operational policy in relation to service users with long term mental health needs.

43. That the local health authority review the arrangements for quality assurance monitoring and clinical audit with Adult Consultant Psychiatrists, having regard to the findings in this Independent Review.

Care in the Community: Health services
44. That both the purchaser and provider health agencies undertake a complete review of all aspects of the planning, delivery and evaluation of their mental health aftercare arrangements.

45. That the interface between forensic and general mental health service provision be reviewed.

Care in the Community: Communications
46. That the local Social Services Department and the local health service review and improve their internal and external information communication systems.

Service Response After the Homicide: Records
47. That the Social Services Department undertake an audit of all service user files to ensure that personal information includes details of a next of kin and/or person to be contacted in case of illness, sudden death or other emergency.

Service Response After the Homicide: Serious incidents
48. That, although statutory authorities should be proactive in offering and providing support arrangements for bereaved or affected families in the case of untoward incidents, where the authority may be felt to be to blame we suggest that arrangements be in place to offer support by an independent person or organisation.

49. That all health and social services providers have in place a plan of action for unexpected death and other untoward incidents.

50. Earlier, we recommend that, where appropriate, Housing Associations accommodating vulnerable people have a role in involving neighbours (with the tenant's consent). Here, we recommend that where a placement has caused distress to neighbours, particularly where a violent incident has occurred, Housing Associations should determine their role in offering support and counselling.

Service Response After the Homicide: Police

51.   That the police, when considering the need for medical treatment under custody procedures, include consideration of the need for psychiatric treatment in the case of prisoners believed to be experiencing mental ill health.

Resource and Service Pressures: Joint commissioning

52.   That the health authority, the family health services authority, social services department and GP fundholders give a firm commitment to the joint commissioning of services for people with severe mental health needs, in the first instance for younger adults (16 to 64 years of age), and agree upon a joint strategy for future provision where the primary emphasis is on prevention, care and aftercare in the community.

53.   That in the process of collaboration with joint commissioning, statutory authority purchasers take a needs-led rather than service-led approach.

54.   When allocating resources (finance, staffing, information, etc) that proper account is taken of the different age structures within different ethnic groups in the district population, as well as socio-economic factors, and measures needed to be taken to eradicate institutional racism.

55.   That the health agencies confirm reprovision plans for those local authority services still based in hospitals.

Resource and Service Pressures: Additional funding

56.   That the local authority and health authority take into account their aggregate budgets for older people, younger adults and children, when determining financial allocation on the basis of priority need and, in so doing, determine whether virement is appropriate and possible in order to meet shortfalls for people who have serious mental health needs.

57.   That the Department of Health, health authority and local authorities give serious consideration to the need for 'bridging monies' to facilitate reprovision and the development of community-based services for Newham residents with severe mental health needs.

58.   That the Department of Health allocate additional funding as essential 'bridging monies' for purposes of local joint commissioning in areas facing the greatest obstacles to change and improvement in mental health provision. Such additional funding could be time limited and reallocatable to other areas.

59.   That the Government review the Personal Social Services Standard Spending Assessment in respect of community care for younger adults (16 to 64 years of age).

Resource and Service Pressures: Advocacy

60.   That the statutory authorities actively promote the development of mental health service user forums throughout all services, together with an independent, ethnically sensitive advocacy service for people with severe mental health needs.

Resource and Service Pressures: Services for women

61.   That health service providers give serious consideration to the safety and needs of the small minority of women who are placed in secure health provision, and to the need for choice of single sex wards in all psychiatric hospitals.

Resource and Service Pressures: Community care plans

62.   That local social services authorities and district health authorities, when publishing Community Care Plans on services for people with mental health needs, identify the number, sex, age and ethnicity, together with need profiles, of inpatients in specialist psychiatric services as well as people living in the community, so that the totality of services, location, and future needs of all service users are included.

63.   That local social services authorities and district health authorities pool their mental health training resources in order to promote and target multi-disciplinary training.

The Brian Doherty Inquiry – Report of the Inquiry Team to the Western Health and Social Services Board

Professor George Fenton (Chair), Mr Eamonn Deane, Mr Stanley Herron and Mr Brendan Mullen – Western Health and Social Services Board, October 1995

Synopsis

In January 1994 Brian Doherty abducted and killed Kieran Hegarty, a young child. Doherty was convicted of manslaughter and kidnapping and sentenced to life imprisonment for manslaughter and 10 years for kidnapping. This offence occurred a few hours after he had discharged himself from hospital against medical advice. Brian Doherty was born in March 1974. At school he was assessed as having special needs because of a mild learning disability. By the time he was 11 years old his mother requested help from social services because he was developing behavioural problems. During the course of the next 10 years Brian Doherty had contact with 20 different agencies which included special schools, children's homes, a training school, young offender institutions, the Probation Service and various hospitals.

Brian Doherty was given a dual diagnosis of a severe personality disorder and mild learning difficulties. Mental health services considered his personality problems to be untreatable and the learning difficulties services regarded him as too 'bright' for inclusion within their remit. He was seen as being a nuisance rather than a serious risk to other people. On the day of the homicide his mental state was assessed and he was not considered to be suffering from a mental illness, nor did his risk to himself or others require his detention in hospital. He was advised to remain in hospital for further assessment but refused to do so. Because his mental impairment was not severe, he could not be detained on these grounds. It was therefore not possible to detain him under Northern Ireland mental health legislation (which differs from the Mental Health Act 1983 in England and Wales).

Recommendations: Doherty Inquiry

1. All new inpatients should be seen by the consultant responsible for their care or a senior psychiatrist deputising for him or her within three days of admission, unless the patient has been examined by the consultant or senior deputy at an outpatient clinic or in the community in the one or two days prior to admission.

2. Management should arrange the consultants' contract to allow more frequent review of inpatients' progress according to the patients' needs.

3. All potential inpatient discharges Contrary to Medical Advice should be discussed with the consultant psychiatrist responsible for their care or a senior deputy.

4. All individuals who discharge themselves Contrary to Medical Advice should be offered an early outpatient clinic review.

5. There should be a recorded review of all patients who discharge themselves at the next multidisciplinary team meeting in order to formulate an aftercare plan and liaise with the relevant community services.

6. A detailed mental state assessment and care plan should be entered in all newly admitted patient's casenotes. This should be updated at least once per week.

7. When individuals who have been detained for assessment are regraded as voluntary patients, there should be a detailed written record of the reasons for regrading.

8. There should be an immediate review of the implementation of the named nurse procedures.

9. The nursing staff should be reminded of their responsibilities in relation to record keeping (UKCC Standards for Records and Record Keeping, 1993).

Co-ordination of Care between Services and across Disciplines
10. The importance of team working between hospital, community and primary care needs emphasis and constant review.

11. A multidisciplinary panel with representatives from all the relevant mental health, mental handicap, social work, probation, and education services should be established to consider the most appropriate care package for at risk patients where there is uncertainty as to which agency should be the one to take the lead caring role. An appropriate Chair for such a panel would be a forensic psychiatrist. The main role of this panel would be to resolve inter-agency disputes and uncertainties about the 'ownership' of people who did not fit into the standard services on offer.

12. The group of patients who do not fit into the conventional services should be carefully defined and referred to the co-ordination panel for allocation to the relevant caring agencies.

Defining a Group of At Risk Patients who need Special Supervision
13. The Mental Health Services and other relevant disciplines in the Western Board area should co-operate to identify patients using defined criteria for at risk patients for inclusion in the supervision group. A specialist team led by a forensic psychiatrist with access to back-up medium secure unit beds should be established. The specialist team should be multidisciplinary in nature.

14. Each supervision group patient should have a keyworker, usually a specially trained community psychiatric nurse with a very limited caseload, and the facility to refer to other members of the team with special expertise.

15. The keyworkers should follow patients across Health and Social Services Board boundaries until responsibility is formally transferred to a local specialist team.

16.   Compulsory supervision will be necessary from time to time using a supervised discharge order. This will require new legislation.

17.   A compatible information system between mental health and social services should be established to facilitate greater continuity of care.

Implications with regard to Northern Ireland Mental Health Legislation
18.   The Department of Health and Social Services (Northern Ireland) should review the 1986 Mental Health Order with the aim of introducing an additional category of mental disorder, namely severe personality disorder. This could follow the wording of the English Mental Health Act 1983 (Section 3): '... *such treatment is likely to alleviate or prevent a deterioration of his condition*'.

19.   All staff likely to use powers under the Mental Health (NI) Order 1986 should have received induction training in its use.

20.   In addition, there should be regular refresher training in the use of the Mental Health (NI) Order 1986.

21.   Training should include full knowledge of the additional guidance contained in the Guide to the Order and the Code of Practice.

22.   In all instances where a voluntary patient is discharging himself or herself Contrary to Medical Advice, consideration should be given to the desirability of using powers to detain for assessment.

23.   All staff likely to use powers under the Mental Health (NI) Order 1986 should have ready access to legal advice concerning any aspects where they are unsure of the interpretation of the Order.

Other Issues
24.   We recommend to the Western Health and Social Services Board that our report is made public.

25.   The report presents an opportunity to engage the public in discussion of wider issues relating to mental health and the role of professionals working within this field.

      We would recommend that the Western Health and Social Services Board take the lead in promoting greater community involvement in mental health services.

The Grey Report
**Report of the Independent Inquiry Team into the Care and Treatment of
Kenneth Grey to East London and the City Health Authority**
*Jane Mishcon (Chair), Dr Donald Dick, Nicholas Welch, Antony Sheehan and
Jane Mackay – East London and The City Health Authority, November 1995*
Synopsis
Kenneth Grey strangled his mother on New Year's Day 1995. He pleaded guilty
to manslaughter on grounds of diminished responsibility. The sentencing judge
concluded that he was suffering from a drug-induced psychosis at the time of the
homicide and that he was no longer showing any signs of mental illness. He was
sentenced to seven years imprisonment, although this sentence was referred to the
Court of Appeal on the grounds that it was unduly lenient.

Kenneth Grey was born in July 1970 to Jamaican immigrant parents. His parents
separated when he was young and he was brought up by his mother having intermittent contact with his father. From the age of 13 he began to smoke cannabis and
later took other illicit drugs. His offending, which dates from the same time,
apparently developed in order to fund his drug habit. In addition to offences of theft
and robbery, he was convicted of three offences of violence, the first occurring at
the age of 15. In June 1994 he was sentenced to 12 months' imprisonment.

At the time of the prison sentence Kenneth Grey had no previous history of mental
illness but his mental state deteriorated while in custody. His earliest date of
release was 25 November 1994 and he was transferred to hospital on 23 November
1994 under Section 47 of the Mental Health Act 1983. On 25 November the
Section 47 was replaced by a Section 2 because it was wrongly believed that the
Section 47 expired on his release date. The inquiry team suggest that this led to
decision making which failed to take account of the seriousness of Kenneth Grey's
problems. Misinterpreting the Mental Health Act led to a failure to implement
S117 aftercare procedures. An incomplete Section 2 assessment led to a failure to
apply the Care Programme Approach. The decision to discharge Kenneth Grey
from the Section 2 seemed to be influenced by the imminence of a Mental Health
Review Tribunal. This would not have been the case had the Section 47 remained
in place. Immediately after the discharge of Kenneth Grey from the Section 2 he
was transferred from a secure ward to an open ward of the hospital as an informal
patient. A few hours later Kenneth Grey went absent without leave.

The confusion surrounding the mental health legislation resulted in confusion
about his legal rights, his care, and his management. Kenneth Grey did not return
to the hospital, nor did anyone assume responsibility for offering him any

aftercare services. The Probation Service still had a statutory duty regarding his licence but were unaware that he was in the community because the hospital did not convey this information to them. The offence took place 30 days later.

Recommendations: Grey Report

1. There should be a continuing education and training programme set up to inform medical, nursing, management, and social services staff about the Mental Health Act 1983, in particular the legal status and rights of patients admitted and detained under one of its sections. Given the frequency of transfers to Hackney Hospital from prison, special emphasis should be placed on the ramifications of those sections of the MHA which deal with the transfer to hospital from court or prison.

2. Any patient transferred under Ss 47/49 should be seen as being subject to a full and comprehensive assessment of their health and social needs in accordance with the CPA3.

3. There should be far greater liaison between prison and hospital upon transfer of patients under section. A written summary of any relevant observed behaviour in the prison (including if possible a copy of any Incident Report form in relation to the prisoner) should be sent to the hospital at the time of transfer. At the very least there should be telephone contact between the Principal Officer on the relevant prison wing and the Charge Nurse on the receiving ward at the hospital to discuss any significant behavioural problems.

4. The Prison medical/nursing notes including copies of the section transfer documents should go straight to the patient's hospital file and remain there until discharge, when they should be photocopied and returned to the prison.

5. The Mental Health Locality Team 'MHLT' (and the Probation Service where already involved) should be informed immediately on the patient's admission to hospital under section.

6. The patient should not be allocated to a Named Nurse who is on leave or off sick at the time of admission to hospital or transfer from one ward to another.

7. The Trust must ensure that all doctors who undertake the role of RMO on a permanent or temporary basis are informed of the full range of responsibilities and duties of an RMO, and those which can and cannot be delegated.

8. The medical and nursing notes should be kept if possible in the same file or at least in the same place so that there is ready access to all relevant information.

9. All relevant information about a patient (such as the name of his RMO, the section of the MHA he is detained under and the date of any removal of the section, the fact that he is AWOL and the date of discharge from the hospital) should be logged onto the hospital computer as soon as possible after such detail comes into existence and should be updated with any change.

10. Copies of any notes/report made by an Approved Social Worker for an assessment prior to an application for a S2 Order should be made available to the hospital within three days and read at the earliest opportunity by the RMO or his junior doctor and the Named Nurse responsible for the patient and kept on the patient's file(s).

11. An assessment pursuant to S2 MHA should be long and full enough to be able (as far as possible) to assess the risks to self and others if the section is discharged. This must include the risk of absconding.

12. Such an assessment should include gathering as much information about the patient from as many sources as possible. If the patient has been transferred from prison, the Probation Service should be contacted to provide any relevant information and a check should be made of his/her antecedents for convictions involving violence.

13. There should be full consultation with nursing staff before any discharge of section and if possible also with any allocated keyworker from the MHLT.

14. No one other than the RMO or another named Consultant can discharge any detention order under the MHA nor grant leave of absence to any compulsorily detained patient. We strongly recommend that this is clearly printed on the forms which need to be signed in order to discharge a section or grant leave of absence.

15. A detention order should not be discharged immediately prior to transfer from a secure ward to an open ward. The section should remain at least long enough for the receiving ward to be able to assess how they need to manage the patient and the risk of absconding/risk to self and others in an open environment.

16. A pending Mental Health Review Tribunal (MHRT) should not be a reason to discharge a section. The following developments are recommended over the operating of MHRTs:

If the patient is transferred to a new ward immediately or very shortly before the tribunal hearing, the reports for the tribunal should be prepared by the practitioners who know him best; there should be regular training for all staff on MHRT procedures and requirements;

The Trust should invite the Mental Health Tribunal Office to join in a review of the working and the outcomes of recent tribunal hearings and procedures in Hackney Hospital, and draw up proposals for development, including those for discussion on the role of MHRTs. We recommend guidelines should be drawn up for the approach in future towards MHRTs.

17. There should be guidelines on good practice and procedures for the transfer and handover of responsibility for patients from one ward to another. These should include:

Identifying a named nurse for the patient on the receiving ward in advance of the transfer who will be 'briefed' prior to the handover on all relevant information to ensure a continuity of care and assessment;

Having an agreed care plan to cover the transfer and the initial stages of the patient's stay on the new ward;

Agreement over the preferred legal status for the patient on transfer.

18. A transfer from a secure to an open ward outside normal working hours should be avoided.

19. The nurse admitting the patient to the new ward should have available and read the nursing/medical notes prior to making their own admission assessment.

20. The patient should be kept under special observation following transfer to an open ward until the staff are satisfied that it is no longer necessary.

21. The Missing Patients Procedure should be implemented in all cases where the patient leaves the ward and nothing is known of their whereabouts. No assumptions should be made that the patient will return to the ward. Managers should monitor the effectiveness and usage of the Missing Patients Procedure.

22. A link should be established between the patient and a member of the MHRT from the time of admission until the time a keyworker is allocated, if one is considered necessary.

23. Any involvement of any member of the MHLT should be construed as a referral to the team as a whole and should be logged immediately.

24. Any keyworker who has been allocated (or a representative if not available) should attend all ward rounds involving their allocated patient and should be part of the decision-making process concerning discharge of a section/ transfer.

25. The discharge summary should be completed by a doctor who knew the patient.

26. A discharge from the hospital should not mean a discharge from the total resource of the mental health service. Once a patient is admitted to hospital they should become the responsibility of the linked catchment locality team until such time as they may be reallocated to a more appropriate team.

27. A case must never be closed and a patient discharged from mental health care in ignorance of the patient's present health and welfare.

28. The Trust should ensure that the Care Programme Approach is fully implemented in line with national guidance, that its implementation is fully audited using available audit tools, and that staff are fully trained to ensure that both the spirit and the letter of the CPA are embraced and adopted.

29. All existing procedures should be reviewed in the light of the discussion and recommendations contained in this report. If there are no procedures in place for areas highlighted in this report, they should be devised and implemented.

30. The Trust should, at the earliest opportunity, set up a meeting with Pentonville Prison medical service, the probation and social services, to discuss the concerns and recommendations outlined in this report. They should further agree an action plan for their implementation and to improve communication and co-operation between their separate agencies.

The Viner Report
The Report of the Independent Inquiry into the Circumstances Surrounding the Deaths of Robert and Muriel Viner
Anthony Harbour (Chair), Dr John Brunning, Linda Bolter and Helen Hally – Dorset Health Commission, September 1995
Synopsis
In April 1995 Robert Viner, aged 42, killed his mother, Muriel Viner, aged 76. He died some hours later from a drug overdose. They had lived together in Mrs Viner's house for nearly 20 years. Shortly after her husband died in 1971, Mrs Viner

moved from Oxfordshire to Dorset where she lived for 21 years. Mrs Viner had two children, Robert and Deborah. Deborah was married and lived in Birmingham. In the early 1970s Robert had left home and gone to university at about the same time that Mrs Viner moved house. She had not expected her son to go and live with her but, after completing his degree in 1975, Robert did so on a temporary basis and never moved away. By this time Robert Viner already had mental health problems. He was referred for psychiatric help in 1971, at the age of 18, and again in 1975, at the time of his university finals. He was re-referred in 1976, by which time he had moved to Dorset.

Gradually a pattern emerged, whereby Robert Viner withdrew socially, and used a variety of prescribed and non-prescribed drugs, including alcohol. He spent much of the day in bed and his self-care deteriorated. He became increasingly dependent on his mother, who seemed to tolerate the inequalities of their relationship with a certain equanimity. He appeared to resent visitors such as his sister whom he saw as an intrusion. It was on a day after one such visit at Easter 1995 that Mrs Viner died from severe head injuries. Robert Viner died shortly afterwards. Robert Viner had no previous history of offending. He received outpatient psychiatric care from 1976 onwards with two short admissions to psychiatric hospital in 1981 and 1982. He had regular visits from CPNs, limited contact with the social services department and the OT service and regular contact with his GP. The last contact with mental health services before Mrs Viner's death was on the day she died, when the CPN visited.

The issues raised by this report include the role of carers and the importance of assessing their needs separately from those of the mental health service user. The report considers that Mrs Viner's 'needs as a carer were never fully identified and were subsequently not responded to' (Viner, 1996, p87). Balancing different needs and rights is a crucial issue in mental health services, which is clearly illustrated in this report. The role of housing and providing appropriate accommodation is a further important factor in the delivery of satisfactory standards of community care. The ability of different agencies and professionals to provide integrated care packages, through multidisciplinary teamwork, underpins service provision to ensure effective care for people with a serious mental illness. This is identified with clarity by the Viner Report.

Recommendations: Viner Report
Occupational Therapy Service
1. Acute OT staff are now integrated into the CMHTs. However, the re-habilitation OT service remains separate both from the acute OT service and from the CMHTs. All agencies need to have a clear understanding of the

role of the rehabilitation OT service and bringing the services professionally closer would promote a more efficient service.

Primary Health Care Teams

2. The GP for any patient subject to the CPA should be provided with a copy of any care plan and informed of any change to that plan.

3. Where a person cared for is subject to the CPA then, subject to consent (and taking into account the needs of confidentiality), the keyworker ought to ensure that the carer's GP is provided with a copy of the care plan.

4. There should be formal arrangement for routine joint review of all the GP practice clients who are in receipt of care from the specialist mental health team. This would allow cases to be discussed and reviewed at practice meetings attended by CPNs.

Accommodation – Housing agencies' record keeping and procedures

5. It is necessary for the individual housing associations which deal with general and special needs housing for vulnerable client groups, to have a clearer appreciation of the role and function of the responsible housing authorities. This will involve the establishment of clear written procedures and appropriate training for staff involved.

6. Increased awareness of the routes which should be followed in dealing with housing applications by persons with mental health problems should be developed. This applies to both social services and health staff and could be addressed by more formal guidelines and appropriate training.

7. In relation to special needs housing, housing agencies should review their information and record-keeping systems wherever there is knowledge of mental health service involvement. This is to ensure that there is an adequate written record of transactions that take place. In a CPA case, the lead agency should be provided with copies of all relevant documents and also the length of time records are kept should be re- evaluated.

Accommodation – Housing co-ordination structures

8. The role of the Housing Liaison Groups in relation to Special Needs Housing should be clearly specified and all relevant professionals should be advised of the Group's function in this area. Attendance of health professionals at these Groups, at operational level, should be reviewed to ensure that there is adequate input from the health services in this process.

Accommodation – Special Needs Housing Database
9.   A high priority should be given to the development and maintenance of the database and the information contained in it should be made available to all relevant professionals who become involved in the housing field. The existence of the database should be publicised, particularly to health keyworkers.

Interagency communication
10.   Any referral by a CPA keyworker for a specific service from another agency should be confirmed in writing and a copy of any care plan should be made available.

Linkages between social services department teams
11.   The social services department should examine the linkages within the service, in particular those between the rehabilitation and mental health teams, and provide guidance to staff on the need to take into account the potential for onward referral between the teams.

Training
12.   All health professionals, who are going to have to undertake a keyworker role under the CPA, should be involved in joint multiagency training with housing and social services staff. The purpose of the training would be to broaden the understanding of the function and role of these two agencies in the accommodation field and to further their understanding of the resources available.

Accessing housing associations
13.   Procedures should be established to deal with all housing applications received by housing associations. These should encompass referral to the social services department or to the relevant CMHTs, and to the housing authority for assessment and prioritisation.

Common housing register
14.   Consideration should be given to establishing a common housing register.

Personal Care Service
15.   Consideration should be given to the development of a discrete personal care service.

Carers – Carer support
16.   The implementation of the existing multiagency initiatives in relation to carer support should be given high priority.

Carers – Confidentiality Policy
17.   An interagency confidentiality policy should be developed which must include reference to the carer's circumstances.

Local policy and guidance on CPA
18.   Steps should be taken to incorporate current guidance into local practice and procedure including the following:

- carers should be involved in planning care

- care plans should be agreed with carers as far as possible

- carers may need their own needs assessed.

Legal Issues – Guardianship
19.   Greater consideration of the use of guardianship under the Mental Health Act 1983 should be given to cases where individuals with long term mental health problems are being supported in the community but are opposed to moving to alternative accommodation. This will require comprehensive multiagency training.

Legal Issues – Multiagency case management
20.   Consideration should be given to establishing protocols and procedures for screening all CPA cases. This is to ensure that the lead agency/authority in a CPA case can evaluate whether the statutory or other duties and obligations imposed on other agencies/authorities are being fulfilled. Similarly, if another agency/authority is asked to assist in a CPA case, that organisation can assess if the request is compatible with their own statutory or other duties.

Training
21.   Multiagency training should be arranged to allow health professionals, who are likely to be keyworkers under the CPA, to understand the resources and legal obligations of social services departments and housing agencies. The legal obligations that are imposed on local authorities in relation to provision for carers should be a matter for particular attention.

Policy Issues – the CPA
22.   All referrals to the social services department should be in writing (this excludes referrals directly to the attached CMHT social worker).

23.   If a referral is made to a social worker within a CMHT then that person must have access to original referral documents and details of any subsequent assessments undertaken.

24. Care plans must be made available to agencies and workers to whom a referral has been made for involvement in mental health care.

25. If the social services department is asked to become involved in a specific piece of work by health professionals, the existing care plan must be made available, evaluated and understood.

26. Consideration needs to be given to the agencies establishing a process for resolving any disagreement that may arise over the implementation of a care plan.

27. In line with national guidance which requires that the CPA is applied to all mentally ill patients who are accepted by the specialist mental health services, existing local joint policy/procedural guidelines on the CPA should be reviewed, to identify the CPA tiers that will be operated locally and to define entry requirements to those tiers with as much precision as possible.

Policy Issues – Risk Assessment
28. Risk assessment training should be extended to all CMHT members.

29. Any assessment under the CPA should include a full appraisal of the situation and potential difficulties of the carer – especially when that person is elderly and the burden of caring is unshared.

Policy Issues – CMHT Development
30. Consideration should be given to the promotion of interagency and inter-disciplinary relationships within the CMHTs. Particular attention should be paid to the management of CMHTs in order to assist the teams to function effectively as integrated units.

Policy Issues – Supervision
31. Attention should be given to the development and implementation of a supervision policy for all mental health professionals, including doctors, of all grades. Also any policy must make explicit the mechanisms that will ensure that every current case managed by a professional is automatically reviewed within a specified period.

Policy Issues – Internal Review
32. Any members of staff, or their managers, involved in direct work with a client, whose case is being investigated, should not be members of the internal review team. The role of these key staff would be to prepare reports and attend to give evidence as necessary.

33.   The Trust should establish serious incident policies and procedures,
       including details of the staff and personnel to be involved in any invest-
       igation and audit.

34.   Trust employees involved in managing reviews/audits should not be from
       the particular branch of the service concerned.

35.   The definition and classification of serious incidents need to be developed.

36.   The process of serious incident reviews/audits needs to be re-evaluated to
       avoid a multiplicity of reviews.

The Case of Jason Mitchell: Report of the Independent Panel of Inquiry
*Louis Blom-Cooper QC (Chair), Adrian Grounds, Pat Guinan, Anne Parker and
Michael Taylor – Duckworth, April 1996*
Synopsis
In December 1994 Jason Mitchell killed Mr and Mrs Wilson, a retired couple, and
subsequently killed his father. He was sentenced to three terms of life imprison-
ment for manslaughter on the grounds of diminished responsibility.

Jason Mitchell was born in July 1970, the youngest of five children. Before he was
a year old his mother left the family, who were then cared for by their father. By the
time he was eight, Jason Mitchell had begun shoplifting and was subsequently
transferred to a special school on account of his truancy and anti-social behaviour.
At the age of 17, Jason Mitchell threatened a pregnant shop assistant with a screw-
driver in the course of committing a robbery from a shop till, for which he received
a two year youth custody sentence. Although he was not diagnosed as suffering
from mental illness at this stage he was seen regularly by a psychiatrist while in
custody. Jason Mitchell was released from custody in 1989. Less than a year later
in 1990 he was charged with attempted murder and other offences and received a
hospital order with a restriction order (Section 37/41) under the Mental Health Act
1983 after the charge had been reduced to one of common assault. A year after this
in 1991, Jason Mitchell received a deferred conditional discharge from a Mental
Health Review Tribunal.

At this stage in his life Jason Mitchell was in hospital in Surrey although his home
area was Suffolk, to where he wished to return. Therefore, arrangements were
made for his transfer as a restricted patient to a hospital in Suffolk so that his
discharge could be planned and supervised. In 1993, the Mental Health Review
Tribunal endorsed the previous tribunal decision and Jason Mitchell moved to
hospital in Suffolk. A year later, in 1994, he was placed in MIND accommodation

and a few months later received his conditional discharge. He later returned to hospital as an informal patient because of behaviour problems at the hostel. One month later, in December 1994, he left the hospital and failed to return.

Recommendations relating to general mental health services: Jason Mitchell Inquiry

1. Significant contributions to clinical assessments by professional staff in disciplines other than psychiatry and nursing should be captured systematically, eg. in the compilation of reports for case conferences, other reviews, and hospital transfers.

2. Social Services Departments which transfer case responsibility for restricted patients should also transfer the case records.

3. In any case where the criminal event involving a mentally disordered person is serious or dangerous, it should be the responsibility of the Crown Prosecution Service to prepare a full account of the criminal event before criminal proceedings have been finalised. The CPS should also ensure that this account is conveyed, after the criminal process has run its course, to all those involved in the criminal proceedings, to clinicians subsequently responsible for the care of the patient, and to C3 Division of the Home Office in respect of restricted cases. The account should become an established part of the patient's clinical record.

4. The Crown Prosecution Service should review its procedures in relation to the prosecution of mentally disordered offenders destined to be routed into the mental health system through a hospital order.

5. The Royal College of Psychiatrists, the Royal College of Nursing, and other relevant professional bodies should issue guidance to their respective members not to rest content with information about the 'index offence' but to inquire thoroughly into the criminal events.

6. Efforts should be made to ensure that the medical members of tribunals dealing with restricted patients are forensic psychiatrists.

7. The third category member of the Mental Health Review Tribunal should be named 'other relevant discipline' and the Lord Chancellor's list should include a number of psychologists.

8. The medical member of the tribunal should expect the hospital to provide a set of summary documents with reports from the professionals involved in the multidisciplinary teams responsible for the patient's care and treatment.

9.   The House of Lords' decision in *Secretary of State for the Home Department v. Oxford Regional Mental Health Review Tribunal (1988)* AC 120 should be reversed by law so as to allow a tribunal to adjourn an application in order to give time for a further examination of the patient's mental health before any decision to discharge is made.

10. Four general measures in respect of restricted patients should be considered by the Home Office:

     (i)   C3 Division of the Home Office should act as a repository of information about the patient's index offence(s);

     (ii)   The procedures and practices of C3 Division could usefully be compared with Home Office practice in relation to Discretionary Lifer Panels;

     (iii) The Notes for the Guidance of Social Supervisors should be reviewed and revised to take account of potential conflicts in the roles of social workers arising from changes in the Community Care, Mental Health and Criminal Justice legislation;

     (iv)   The Case Worker Guide should be updated to require information not just from the RMO but from others who will bear responsibility for the aftercare of the patient.

11. The Department of Health should draw together the existing fragmented policy guidance on the role of Local Authority and Health Services staff in the care and after-care of mentally ill people in an integrated document of guidance.

12. Internal reviews of practice following major untoward events should be conducted by a manager with no direct line management responsibility for the case in question.

13. Given the need for close networking between many agencies and the establishment of supervision registers, some thought should be given by the Department of Health and the professional bodies to drawing on the best practice from child protection in developing an interagency approach to case management for mentally ill patients who are discharged into the community.

14. Inpatient units whose patients include offenders with disturbed personalities should have access to specialist psychodynamic expertise.

15. In respect of behaviour modification programmes and particularly in the absence of valid patient consent, a locally agreed procedure should be adopted in which the RMO should seek the advice of a suitably qualified person who is not a member of the clinical team responsible for the patient. This will normally be a psychologist, although some medical staff, social workers and nurses have received special training that equips them to supervise psychological procedures.

16. RMOs and clinicians managing offender patients should afford such patients regular reviews in private.

17. All Police Forces should have formal Missing Patients Procedures agreed with local hospitals and Social Services, and within these a system for inquiring into the circumstances of repeated absconding by detained patients, particularly those subject to restriction orders.

18. The 'Appropriate Adult' system in criminal justice should be re-examined with a view to extending its role.

19. Employers, their legal advisers and insurers should find ways of helping their staff make direct personal contact with bereaved families, unless the families do not wish for this.

20. All authorities mandated to set up inquiries under NHS Executive Guidance HSG(94)27 of 10 May 1994 should actively consider including in their Terms of Reference directions that families of the victims should be given the opportunity to be present at any Inquiry into homicide, whether the Inquiry is held in public or private.

21. A more direct, proactive and individual approach to the members of victims' families should be adopted by all agencies engaged in crisis support work following homicides and similar events.

22. The Secretary of State for Health should set in train a review of the Mental Health Review Tribunal system in the context of a review of the Mental Health Act 1983.

23. Police Forces nation-wide should commit themselves to adopting the training and policies for dealing with mentally ill people, as currently practised within the Metropolitan Police.

24. Any social services worker assigned the task of social supervisor of a restricted patient should be an Approved Social Worker.

25.   The relevant Government departments should set a target date by which
      time all social supervisors of restricted patients will have acquired the com-
      petencies in forensic social work set out by CCETSW.

26.   The Department of Health should ensure the funding of adequate numbers
      of training places for Clinical Psychologists.

27.   All trainees in General Psychiatry should spend a period of training in a
      forensic psychiatric service under the supervision of a Forensic Psychiatrist.

28.   General Psychiatrists taking up consultant posts with responsibility for
      secure beds should have had a period of training in forensic psychiatry.

29.   Arrangements for psychiatric training both nationally and locally in Suffolk
      and in the Anglia and Oxford Regions, should be reviewed and, if
      necessary, enhanced so as to ensure that all trainees in general psychiatry
      receive adequate clinical training and experience in psychodynamic and
      forensic aspects of psychiatry.

30.   Attention should be given to identifying and meeting more thoroughly the
      training needs of existing as well as new Mental Health Review Tribunal
      members.

31.   Tribunal members should be informed about the clinical outcomes for
      patients following discharge decisions, and confidential retrospective
      reviews should be held in cases where patients re-offend seriously after
      discharge.

32.   There should be greater clarity and explicitness in the guidance concerning
      the disclosure of documents to public inquiries.

33.   The Rules of the Supreme Court-Order 38, rule 19(1) – which authorises the
      Crown Office to issue a subpoena 'in aid of an inferior court or tribunal' –
      should be reviewed by the Rules Committee to make it clear that non-
      statutory public inquiries, set up by central or local Government, qualify for
      subpoena powers.

34.   The Prison Service should ensure, by the end of 1996, that it has in place a
      database and a fully effective system whereby prisoners' IMRs, including
      those of remand prisoners, follow them wherever they may be in the system.
      The provision should encompass access to the system for all those involved
      in the penal system.

35. The question of confidentiality of prison medical records should be fully reviewed. As a first step towards such review, the General Medical Council and other professional bodies should be asked for their views.

36. The Government should consider establishing an independent committee to review the subject of the supply and dissemination of information within the services dealing with people in need of treatment, care and control.

Recommendations relating to local services: Jason Mitchell Inquiry

37. The Health Authority invites the members of the Inquiry Panel to reconvene, in private, within six months of publication of this report to consider the responses, both official and unofficial, to the recommendations; and to report activity to the Health Authority early in 1997.

38. Case conferences should be recorded more fully.

39. Where a breakdown in a community placement occurs, the existing review systems should be implemented.

40. Health and Social Service Purchasers should review the balance of expenditure to see if a more specialised focus could be developed within the range of community-based residential services in order to provide a locally based therapeutic service.

41. The Purchasing Authority should consider developing quality standards applicable to the care of patients with histories of violent offending. Such standards might include requiring Providers to ensure that a full range of assessment approaches, including access to forensic psychiatry services, is available to such patients.

42. An externally facilitated multidisciplinary review should be undertaken of the balance between behavioural and psychodynamic approaches at the local hospital and the skills available to develop a greater degree of flexibility.

43. External, peer group audit should be incorporated into the Trust's quality assurance programme; and the Purchasers, perhaps in concert with the Department of Health, should develop contract monitoring measures more finely tuned to the needs of services for people with mental health problems.

44. Purchasers should ensure that there is clinical audit of hospital psychiatric teams to examine multidisciplinary working and the representation of varied and possibly contradictory perspectives in clinical records.

45.   Purchasers of social care should ensure that an adequate supply of forensic social work is available in their area.

46.   The local Health Authority should review whether the availability of forensic psychiatry services is sufficient.

Report of the Independent Team Inquiry into the Care and Treatment of NG
John Main QC (Chair), Dr John Wilkins, David Pope and Steve Manikon – Ealing, Hammersmith & Hounslow Health Authority, April 1996
Synopsis
In September 1994 NG ran over and killed SK, a stranger. He was charged with murder but was found unfit to plead and was detained in a high secure hospital.

NG was born in Kenya in June 1958. He came to the UK with his family at the age of 12. Subsequently he obtained a degree and worked as a pharmacist for five years. He married in 1982 and had a son, but lost contact with both his wife and son after he became divorced in 1986. Symptoms of a developing mental illness were first noticed by his family in 1982. In 1984 he was diagnosed as suffering from paranoid schizophrenia. His offending history dates from 1985, when he was placed on probation for forging prescriptions.

A year later he attacked his wife and attempted to kidnap his son and was detained in hospital for three months under Section 3 of the MHA 1983. In 1989 he assaulted his father. In 1990 he travelled abroad but the evidence suggests he was acutely ill at the time. By 1991 his social circumstances were deteriorating further because of his illness and he was compulsorily detained in hospital for a third time. He was reluctant to accept medication but relapsed quickly without it. He was admitted to hospital on a fourth occasion following an overdose at the end of 1993. He was discharged to the day hospital in March 1994 with social work support. By this time Care Programme Approach procedures had been adopted. In June 1994 he was discharged from the day hospital with social work follow-up and attendance at a day centre and work centre.

By August 1994 NG's mental state was noted to be deteriorating and a referral to the CPN service was made. His social worker went on annual leave but without providing any cover arrangements. Complaints were made by NG's neighbour to the housing association and to social services. It was decided that this matter could be left until the social worker returned from leave. Further concerns were noted by the drop-in centre and communicated to social services in the social worker's absence. On his return from leave the social worker acted on these messages and visited NG at home. Although NG was thought to be paranoid and in an agitated state, he was not considered 'sectionable'. He was reassessed by the social worker again within a few days because of further concerns, expressed by the neighbour. However, NG's 'possible need for hospital treatment was not met' (NG Report, 1996, p41). On 6 September he attended the drop-in centre in the morning and later ran over a woman in a car park.

Several problems were identified by the report. For example, the CPA was inadequately implemented, with little evidence of multidisciplinary teamwork. The keyworker was not clearly identified, leading to delays and confusion. NG was reluctant to take oral medication and was not receiving medication in depot form. Issues about arranging cover while the keyworker was on leave were highlighted. Also the fact that NG was allowed to drive his car when his mental state had become so unstable was an additional factor in this particular tragedy.

Recommendations: NG Report

1. All persons known to suffer from severe mental disorder should continue to receive appropriate support from a multidisciplinary mental health team and should not be expected to rely on the duty social worker for assistance.

2. Anger management therapy should only be undertaken by or under the close supervision of experienced qualified staff. Failure of this form of treatment should lead to a consideration of alternative treatments including referral to a specialist centre.

3. The Chief Executive of the Trust ensures that the issue of consultant responsibility of the Day Hospital is resolved without delay.

4. All statutory, voluntary and independent agencies (particularly including general practitioners) likely to be involved in the care of patients subject to the CPA procedure should be invited to attend CPA meetings and should receive copies of the record of the meeting whether they attend or not.

5. As well as the user, all likely carers of patients subject to the CPA procedure should be invited to attend CPA meetings and should receive copies of the record of the meeting whether they attend or not.

6. The risk assessment should be an integral part of the CPA documentation circulated.

7. The CPA documentation should include information as to the nature of the patient's medication (at least indicating whether it is taken orally or by depot injection). In line with the recommendations made in other inquiry reports, we recommend that all members of the team should be alerted to the signs and symptoms in the patient which may indicate that the patient is likely to relapse. These indications may be identified by the doctors, the patient or carers. Non-compliance with medication should be recognised as a significant pointer to a relapse.

8. A deputy for the keyworker should be identified and the identity recorded at the CPA meeting and the keyworker and deputy should not be on holiday simultaneously without making specific arrangements for cover. These should include provisions for handover and for notification to all concerned.

9. All referrals to the drop-in centre (run by a voluntary agency) of patients subject to the CPA procedure should be accompanied by full CPA documentation.

10. All referrals to any day care resource of patients subject to the CPA procedure should be accompanied by full CPA documentation.

11. Outpatient reviews of patients subject to the CPA procedure should be under the close supervision of the responsible consultant and doctors without the qualification MRCPsych should not assess patients except under supervision.

12. We recommend that the Trust and SSD develop a costed and timescaled strategic plan for the development and implementation of integrated multi-disciplinary Community and Mental Health Teams as soon as is practicable.

13. Professional supervision and managerial support should be readily available to Community Mental Health Centre and Team Managers. CPN caseloads should be kept under review and CPN record keeping should be subjected to an internal audit process.

14. All personnel having to do with the operation of the Mental Health Act should be reminded at the earliest possible opportunity that the words used in Sections 2 and 3 of the Act are 'health *or* safety' and not 'health *and* safety'.

15. The Medical Director of the Trust in consultation with the medical staff and with their agreement should implement a policy whereby consultants and junior doctors should so arrange their leave that no more than one medical

member of a team is away at any one time. A consultant who is going on leave should ensure that the keyworker for all patients subject to the CPA procedure is aware of the arrangements made for cover.

16. The Medical Director of the Trust should formulate and circulate a clear policy statement indicating the circumstances in which it would be appropriate for professional staff to notify DVLA of the illness of a patient.

17. Consideration should be given to the desirability of including in the CPA documentation a note of the advice given to the patient about driving.

The Hampshire Report – Report of the Independent Inquiry Team into the Care and Treatment to Redbridge and Waltham Forest Health Authority
Jane Mishcon (Chair), Dr Donald Dick, Ian Milne, Paul Beard and Jane Mackay
Redbridge and Waltham Forest Health Authority, May 1996
Synopsis
Francis Hampshire killed his wife Catherine Hampshire in a frenzied knife attack on 31 May 1994. He was found guilty of manslaughter on the grounds of diminished responsibility and detained under Section 37/41 of the MHA 1983.

The couple had been married for nearly 40 years and had four adult children living away from home. Francis Hampshire was born in October 1933. Both he and his wife were teachers. Mr Hampshire retired on grounds of ill health in 1986, at which time he was head of the French Department at the school at which he worked. Mrs Hampshire continued working and was Head of the Special Needs Department at a Catholic school and was also Deputy Head of the school when she died. She also became sole carer for her husband. Towards the end of the 1970s, Frank Hampshire was treated for anxiety and depression by his GP and was referred to psychiatrists on three occasions between 1977 and 1979. At the time he refused hospital admission.

The first evidence of serious mental health problems for Frank Hampshire was noticed in 1983, and in 1985 his GP again referred him for a psychiatric opinion and once more he refused admission to hospital. This was the first time symptoms of paranoid delusional thinking became apparent. A pattern of Mr Hampshire underestimating the severity of his illness and refusing admission to hospital was a recurring pattern throughout his illness. His paranoid belief system persisted and if his wife sought help` she was seen by Mr Hampshire as conspiring against him. In March 1986, Frank Hampshire attacked his wife and threatened to kill her and following this incident he was admitted to hospital compulsorily under Section 2 of the Mental Health Act 1983. After he was discharged CPN follow-up was arranged. Initially he complied with medication, but refused to take his depot medication in 1988.

He responded well to anti-psychotic medication but relapsed quickly without it. His insight into his illness was poor. He did, however, agree to informal admission to hospital as a result of extreme family pressure in 1993. In March 1994 an urgent referral to the senior CPN was made, who visited the following day. By April 1994, the CPN wrote that she could 'only monitor the situation as Frank refuses to enter into any active care plan' (Hampshire, 1996, p35). However, as events were to show, 'monitoring was not enough' (Hampshire, 1996, p53). The CPN went on annual leave in May arranging to visit again on her return at the beginning of June. 'No proactive arrangements were made for a visit to the Hampshires during [the CPN's] absence' (Hampshire, 1996, p39). Before the CPN returned from leave the tragedy had happened.

Recommendations: Hampshire Report
To the Trust and Health Authority
1. Mental Health Care must be given a higher priority within the Trust and the Health Authority.

2. The Chair of the Trust and the Chair of the Health Authority must make a joint visit to [the hospital ward in question] to see for themselves the unacceptable conditions to which patients are being admitted.

3. The Health Authority in conjunction with other local agencies must take steps to secure radical improvements to Mental Health services.
    The following should be taken into account:

    (a)   the implications of the new Mental Health (Patients in the Community) Act 1995

    (b)   the NHSE Guidance on the Care Programme Approach and the development of a spectrum of mental health services

    (c)   the adverse observations about mental health services within the area made over several years by the Mental Health Act Commission and the local Community Health Council

    (d)   the lack of community facilities and alternatives to inpatient care

    (e)   the deplorable state of the hospital ward in question.

4. As soon as possible after an incident involving a homicide by a patient (including an outpatient) in the care of the psychiatric services, there should be:

    (a)   a clinical audit at immediate service level under the management of a clinician not involved in providing care for the patient, and

(b)   an internal inquiry. The treating clinical staff (including any Community Psychiatric Nurses who have been involved in the care of the patient) should be interviewed and detailed statements taken from them.

5.   Professional debriefing and access to counselling should be offered by the Health Authority to any member of the clinical team who expresses a wish to receive it.

6.   The immediate family of the patient should be invited at the earliest opportunity to discuss any matters relating to the care and treatment of the patient. Support should be offered to any member of the clinical team who agrees to meet with any such relative.

7.   Counselling or alternative support should be offered by the health authority to any member of the patient's family who expresses a need for such help.

8.   An Independent Inquiry must be set up at an early enough stage for the Panel to be able to start its investigations as soon as the outcome of any criminal proceedings is known.

9.   The consent of the patient to the release of all relevant records should be obtained at the earliest possible date and all such records should be acquired and delivered to the Inquiry Panel members in advance of the commencement of the Independent Inquiry.

10.   The Trust should ensure that all members of the clinical psychiatric team (at all levels) have access to proper clinical supervision, preferably entirely independent of their own workload. We do not consider the present arrangements (monthly formal meetings between the consultant psychiatrist and the CPN team manager and informal discussions between the treating doctors and the CPNs at weekly ward rounds) to be adequate.

To the Clinical Team

11.   The clinicians have a clear responsibility to seek the views of the immediate family in a situation where the medical opinion is that the patient should be in hospital and the patient refuses informal admission. The family should be involved if possible in the taking of any history and in the assessment of the patient's current condition especially when the patient is being cared for in the community and is refusing or unable to attend outpatient appointments. A proper risk assessment should always include the views of the family where possible.

12.   If a patient has missed more than two outpatient appointments, the clinical team must follow up to establish the reason for such non-attendance.

13.   If the treating doctor examines the patient and is of the opinion that the patient needs hospitalisation, is not at that time sectionable, and is refusing to be admitted informally there must be a continuous process of risk assessment which must include regular face-to-face review by the clinicians. Part of that assessment must include the health and safety of any carer. Clinicians should be encouraged to try to identify patterns in the patient's mood and behaviour. An assessment must not be made over the telephone.

14.   As part of the risk assessment which must be carried out by the clinical team, consideration should be given to referral to an Approved Social Worker to carry out an assessment.

15.   The clinical team should inform the patient's nearest relatives of their right to request such an assessment themselves where the carer believes that the patient should be in hospital and the patient is refusing any admission offered.

16.   Relatives must be made aware that they have free access to the clinical team and should be encouraged to contact them with any concerns about the patient or his/her carer.

17.   Any proper care plan must contain a contingency plan to be put into effect in the event of the failure of the primary plan. A multiagency case conference should be held if the situation is complex enough to warrant it.

18.   Where a community psychiatric nurse (CPN) is sent in by the treating doctors to assess the patient who they believe should be in hospital, ie. to be the eyes and ears of the clinical team, a detailed record of what is seen and heard at each visit must be sent to the doctors as soon as possible, with copies to the GP.

19.   All relevant clinical information about the patient should be passed between the treating psychiatrists, the GP, the CPN, and Social Services, where involved.

20.   No CPN with primary responsibility for a patient should go on leave without making cover arrangements for high priority patients and without notifying the patient's GP.

The Report of the Inquiry into the Care and Treatment of Shaun Anthony Armstrong
Mr C J Freeman (Chair), Mr A Brown, Dr D Dunleavy and Mr F Graham – Tees District Health Authority, June 1996
Synopsis
In June 1994 Rosie Palmer, aged almost four years, went out to an ice-cream van near to her home to buy an ice-cream and did not return. Three days later her body was found at the home of Shaun Armstrong who lived approximately 50 yards away. Rosie had been sexually abused and her body had been mutilated following her death. Armstrong was sentenced to life imprisonment, having pleaded guilty to murder, and went to prison.

Shaun Armstrong was born in June 1962 to an 18-year-old, whose father was also his own father. His mother had apparently suffered from psychiatric problems from the age of 14 and for the first three years of his life he was brought up by his maternal grandparents. When he was three years old his mother married George Armstrong and Shaun Armstrong was subsequently brought up to believe that George Armstrong was his father. At the age of seven his behaviour deteriorated after a cousin the same age as himself and to whom he was close, died in a road accident. Soon after this he was subjected to sexual abuse by his mother which continued until he was 16. His mother divorced, remarried, and later separated. By the age of 16 his behaviour was very disturbed and he was referred for child guidance. His offending history began about the same time (for offences of dishonesty).

He married in 1981, the marriage breaking down in 1982. From 1982 he was admitted to psychiatric hospitals on several occasions. He was still being offered outpatient appointments at the time of Rosie's murder. He was diagnosed as suffering from personality disorder with addiction problems. His offending behaviour continued and by 1985 he was sentenced to his first term of imprisonment. He had no official record of sexual offences. In 1989, when Armstrong was 27, his mother became terminally ill and disclosed to her son the identity of his natural father. Armstrong had remarried by then and again the marriage broke down. Different reasons were given but allegations of violence to his partners and sexual abuse of his stepdaughters were made. Alongside this history of extreme dysfunction, Armstrong also had a serious problem of alcohol and drug dependency. In 1992 child protection issues were raised by the relevant agencies. Armstrong was no longer living at his wife's address and no contact was allowed with the child he was alleged to have abused. He was interviewed by the police but denied all the allegations and, with no other evidence, no further action was taken. (The child was too young to be interviewed.)

In August 1993, Shaun Armstrong had been rehoused by his local housing department to a one-bedroom maisonette. The housing department had a statutory duty to house him because of his vulnerability. However, they were unaware of his criminal history which in any case had been of a relatively petty nature. The consultant's letter did not refer to any previous violence or abuse.

Recommendations: Armstrong Inquiry
Clinical History Taking – Medical History
1. The Responsible Medical Officer must ensure that recorded case histories are both comprehensive and accurate and that casenotes are regularly updated. Particular attention must be paid to the initial history and inadequacies rectified at the earliest opportunity.

Clinical History Taking – Nursing History
2. Nurses must ensure that a comprehensive history is taken on admission and updated regularly and in our view the Roper-Logan-Tierney model is not suitable for the recording of this information in Psychiatry.

3. There must be adequate supervision of the history taking exercise and recording of information when it is undertaken by a student nurse.

Clinical History Taking – Social History
4. The opportunity must exist at the general hospital in question for the medical and nursing history to be amplified by a social work history when considered appropriate.

Communications – Community Mental Health Team
5. Communications within a multidisciplinary team are fostered when there is a constant membership. The social work membership of the Hartlepool teams is not currently constituted like that and we recommend that their functioning is continually audited and altered in line with other Cleveland Community Mental Health Teams if considered necessary.

Communications – In Ward Setting
6. The role and responsibilities of nursing staff at all levels should be clarified in order to facilitate improved communication.

Communications – Intra-Hospital
7. Patients admitted to the acute unit with episodes of self-harm should be automatically notified to the in-patient psychiatric unit, the RMO (if applicable) and to the General Practitioner.

Communications – Discharge Letters

8.   The discharge letters should contain five key points, namely: diagnosis; treatment; follow up arrangements; prognosis; and concise explanation of the condition.

9.   There should be some system of monitoring discharge letters written by junior medical staff.

Issue of Self-referral to Drug and Alcohol Counselling Agencies

10.   More direct action should be taken to ensure that referrals to drug and alcohol agencies are made and that the initiative is not left to the patient alone. It is, however, accepted that individual patient commitment and responsibility are equally important.

External Agencies

11.   External agencies (eg. the Police, Social Services, etc) should communicate with the RMO when they are investigating an inpatient who is known to be under the RMO's care.

Reappointments on Failure to Attend

12.   The recommended actions of the Trust's internal inquiry, ie. that audit should occur and that reappointments should be within two months at the outside, ought to be implemented as soon as possible.

Care Programme Approach/Risk Assessment

13.   That managers of the appropriate agencies ensure that all staff who are involved in the implementation of the Care Programme Approach are trained in risk assessment.

Audit of Services

14.   That the Health Authority and the Trust continue to monitor the quality of the service and ensure that corrective action takes place.

Additional Recommendation

15.   Consideration should be given at the highest possible level to the possibility of giving inquiries the power to subpoena witnesses and documents.

Report of the Inquiry into the Treatment and Care of Raymond Sinclair
Richard Lingham (Chair), Julian Candy and John Bray – West Kent Health Authority and Kent County Council Social Services, June 1996
Synopsis
In November 1994 Raymond Sinclair killed his mother, Mary Povey. He was convicted of manslaughter on grounds of diminished responsibility and detained under Section 37/41 of the MHA 1983.

He was born in December 1961, the sixth of nine children. His father died when he was 14. It is thought that Mr Povey suffered from paranoid schizophrenia and that the children were abused by him both physically and sexually. Mrs Povey was unable to cope with her large family and after her husband's death was admitted to hospital on several occasions following suicide attempts and threats. Home conditions were characterised by poverty and instability. All the children with the exception of the eldest moved in and out of local authority care or were subject to supervision orders from 1969 onwards. As adults several of Raymond's brothers and sisters have required inpatient hospital treatment for psychiatric problems.

Raymond Povey changed his name to Sinclair when he was in his early 20s because of his family's notoriety (later this made it more difficult to provide a comprehensive history from earlier records). His offending history dates from 1972, mainly that of theft and burglary. He has no record of offences of violence and had not previously been in prison. Excessive alcohol consumption and illicit drug use were noted to be a problem. For nine years from 1983 Raymond Sinclair had a long-term relationship and two children were born in 1986 and 1988. By 1992 this relationship had broken down and evidence of his psychotic illness emerged in 1993. He was first admitted to hospital for psychiatric treatment in April 1994. During the next 30 weeks Raymond Sinclair received a variety of inpatient and community-based services as a result of his developing mental illness. The principal failure in this case is considered to be an organisational one.

Mrs Povey, aged 64, lived in a one-bedroomed flat. Raymond was discharged to his mother's address from hospital despite the inadequacy of this arrangement. The degree of overcrowding was increased as a result of one of Raymond's brothers also staying there temporarily. Although the family cared for Raymond to a very considerable extent they were not central to the aftercare plan nor were their views given much weight. The importance of involving carers in providing appropriate care is one of the findings of several inquiries, including this one.

Recommendations: Sinclair Inquiry
Local Policy Implications
1. The area director should ensure that staff numbers and experience are not allowed to fall so critically low in small outposted teams. The factors affecting recruitment in this locality should be kept under review by the Director of Social Services.

2. The Trust and its purchasing authority should urgently complete and implement plans to build a new acute inpatient unit of appropriate size, and should endeavour to recruit sufficient senior medical staff at both consultant and sub-consultant grades.

3. The Trust Board should require the Director of Mental Health to satisfy them that all working practices and structures foster communication between professionals, and that senior doctors play a full part in CMHTs.

4. Consultants should ensure that trainee doctors are regularly supervised and that the job descriptions of both reflect this commitment.

5. The Medical Director, in consultation with his colleagues and the Director of Medical Services, should draw up a revised job description for the senior registrar posts, defining their role within the medical teams in relation to clinical work, the supervision of more junior staff, and deputising for the Consultant.

6. The Trust's Manager responsible for Nursing Services should ensure that nursing recording sheets are easy for all professionals to understand, and should encourage nursing staff to assemble all relevant information and to pass it on in full at ward rounds.

7. The Director of Mental Health Services should ensure that all professionals working in CMHTs receive appropriate, continuing, and specific training, and are given regular and recorded supervision, relating both to individual cases and to their caseload more generally. Nurses in particular should receive training on one of the many courses now available for CMHNs, for example the Thorn programmes and at the Sainsbury Centre.

8. The Chief Executive of the Trust and the Area Director of Social Services should initiate a joint review to define the specific consequences resulting from the separate functioning of the CMHT (health) and CMHT (social services). Fail-safe mechanisms should be introduced to cover any remaining gaps. The route for all staff to have access to expert medical advice, especially in forensic issues, should be established.

National Policy Implications in Service Provision,
Training and Staff Development

9. i) The information and social histories gathered following admission should always consider the views of other family members, carers, and persons close to the patient. Their views should also be sought when Care Programme Approach plans are made before discharge and when they are reviewed after it. The only exception should be when the patient has made a formal declaration of unwillingness to be involved.

    ii) Keyworkers should receive training in the most effective ways of establishing these communicating links and of managing the sometimes delicate ethical issues involved in maintaining them. This process should be incorporated in the checklist of subjects discussed with their work supervisors.

iii) Those persons who conduct internal investigations and independent inquiries under NHE circular HSG(94)27 should always make early contact with family members, carers, people close to the patient, and any victims to receive their views and information. They should keep them advised of progress and informed of the outcome of the Inquiry.

10. Keyworkers under the Care Programme Approach should only be eligible for appointment when they are competent to (i) identify and record symptoms which may represent significant risk; (ii) discuss these immediately with their supervisors or an experienced worker; (iii) convey their concerns to a consultant psychiatrist or other doctor approved under Section 12 of the Mental Health Act.

11. Directors of Mental Health Services and Directors of Social Services should ensure that all professional staff who work with psychiatric patients become familiar, and remain familiar, with the indicators of dangerousness, and are confident of what action to take should they encounter them.

National Health Services Executive Implications

12. i) A panel should be set up to supervise inquiries commissioned under Health Service Guidelines HSG(94)27.

ii) The panel should be responsible for creating a register of those suitably qualified, both professionally and in their interpersonal skills, to sit on such inquiries.

iii) It should also publish a recommended form of procedure and additional guidance designed to reduce delay and the stress caused to witnesses, particularly the relatives of the deceased and other victims, and to encourage cost-effectiveness.

The Mabota Report – Report of the Independent Inquiry Team into the Care and Treatment of Kumbi Mabota to Redbridge and Waltham Forest Health Authority
Derek Holwill (Chair), Dr David Ndegwa, Shirley Stanner, Nicholas Welch and Jane Mackay – Redbridge and Waltham Forest Health Authority, September 1996
Synopsis
Kumbi Mabota was convicted of the murder of Lidie Njoli Diema at a second trial. (The jury were unable to agree a verdict at the first one.) Mr Mabota still denies

any involvement with Lidie's murder. Lidie was found dead on 16 April 1994, having been kicked and beaten to death and had sustained a large number of wounds to her back.

Kumbi Mabota was born in Zaïre in November 1964. He speaks several languages, English being his fifth and French his fourth. He had five siblings, one of whom has died. The other four live in Paris and remain in contact with him. Mr Mabota joined his family in Paris in 1987, and in 1988 he married Lasamba Bidi (Henriette). He was deported in 1990 or 1991, and was accompanied back to Zaïre by Henriette and his two stepdaughters. Kumbi Mabota's parents were both killed by the military in Zaïre in September 1991.

Following the deaths of his parents he arrived in the UK via Belgium. Henriette and Kumbi Mabota had a son born in June 1993 but who died in May 1994. He had met Lidie in Zaïre in 1991. His relationship with Henriette began to break down and Lidie came to live with him in England at the end of 1993. Lidie became pregnant, but had the pregnancy terminated. The precise nature of the relationships between Kumbi Mabota and Henriette and Lidie remains unclear.

Meanwhile, Kumbi Mabota had problems with obtaining DSS benefits, leading to him spending 48 hours in police custody. Soon after, he was arrested for fraud and remanded in custody for a month in March 1994 before obtaining bail. It is reported that during this period in custody he heard from Lidie to say the pregnancy had been terminated and this led him to feel suicidal. Two weeks after his release from prison he went to Lidie's flat and threatened her with a knife. The police were called. Lidie was injured in the struggle but Mr Mabota also attempted to kill himself by drinking a large quantity of bleach. He was therefore admitted to hospital. After a psychiatric assessment he was transferred to a locked ward for seven days. Shortly after he was transferred back to an open ward he absconded, and Lidie was found murdered a few hours later. Until April 1994, Kumbi Mabota had no prior contact with psychiatric services.

Recommendations: Mabota Report
1. (a) The practice of maintaining medical and nursing notes in different physical locations be discontinued – we consider it of paramount importance that the medical and nursing notes are unitary.

   (b) There should be some system adopted for 'flagging up' key inform-ation relevant to the assessment of possible risk to self or others.

2. In the event of a patient being transferred from hospital to hospital, the patient's notes ought to be transferred with that patient.

3.   (a)   Steps be taken to ensure that nursing care plans are drawn up and re-evaluated on a regular basis, in particular to ensure that they incorporate recommendations made by medical staff; and

     (b)   That there should be a review of the working of the Named Nurse system and that steps should be taken to ensure that the purposes underlying the system are fully understood, so that the system operates otherwise than just in name.

4.   In addition to auditing policies and procedures, the holder of the newly created post in Nursing Research and Development has an opportunity to audit current documentation and make improvements.

5.   Steps be taken to establish standards of minimum competence for interpreting staff ensuring not only competence in the relevant foreign language but also a high degree of familiarity with the English language. There is a need for the clear identification of the competencies necessary for someone to be an effective interpreter in a psychiatric or mental health context.

6.   Attempts be made to improve liaison and information exchange with the Police wherever possible and that staff be encouraged to make contact in appropriate cases.

7.   Steps are taken to implement procedures to ensure that all medical staff, particularly locums being used to cover for existing medical staff, are fully aware of all relevant operational policies.

8.   If and in so far as the system of regular attendance at ward rounds by social workers, with each ward having designated social work cover, does not presently operate, steps should be taken to revive this system.

9.   Bus companies with services visiting psychiatric hospitals are advised of the potential risk of patients absconding and are asked to ensure that drivers are alert to the possibility of patients seeking to abscond by boarding one of their buses.

10. In the event of a serious incident, psychological support, debriefing sessions or post-traumatic stress counselling are co-ordinated and made available to the staff.

Caring for the Carer – Report of Committee of Inquiry to Tees Health Authority - *Richard Barlow (Chair), John Crook, David Kingdon and Peter McGinnis – Tees Health Authority, September 1996*
Synopsis
On 16 February 1995 Keith Taylor stabbed and killed his father, William Taylor.

He pleaded guilty to manslaughter on grounds of diminished responsibility and is now subject to a hospital order with a restriction order. Keith Taylor was born on 18 February 1948 and has three siblings who married and have families of their own. Keith Taylor suffered from epilepsy and lived a sheltered life at home with his parents. He worked for the Gas Board/British Gas from 1964 until 1995. Keith Taylor's mother died from lung cancer in March 1994. She had a history of psychiatric problems, having suffered from a chronic phobic anxiety state. At the same time as Mrs Taylor was terminally ill, William Taylor, her husband, was suffering from dementia, although the severity of his condition was concealed by Mrs Taylor who succeeded in minimising the extent of his confusion. William Taylor's difficulties only became apparent to the rest of the family when he did not understand that his wife had died and constantly asked for her.

When Mrs Taylor died, Keith Taylor faced not only her death but also the task of providing care for his dementing father. He gave up his job to provide full-time care for his father and eventually the stress of so doing led to a deterioration in his own mental health. This led to him being admitted to hospital for psychiatric treatment on three occasions. The first of these admissions to hospital took place in April 1994 when he was detained under Section 2 of the Mental Health Act 1983. He had developed an acute psychotic illness but was denying he was ill. The team caring for William Taylor 'failed to become aware of Keith Taylor's second and third admissions to hospital' (Taylor, 1996, p27). Keith Taylor's second hospital admission, which was informal, took place in May 1994 because of his suicidal thoughts. Keith Taylor's grandmother had died when he was 23 and he seemed to develop some delusional beliefs about this including a belief that something significant would happen to him when he was 46 or 69 years of age. Delusions about his grandmother were noted during this admission but the staff remained unaware of the possible implications.

No CPA procedures were applied despite two hospital admissions in quick succession. His third admission took place in September 1994. A brief episode of psychosis quickly settled and he was discharged without much thought to his needs in the community or the problems he was facing at home. Social services continued to offer help for his father, but this was not accepted by Keith Taylor. The report concludes that hospital staff failed to ensure that Keith Taylor received support after his second and third hospital discharges. Social services were not informed of the complete picture and were therefore not in a position to respond appropriately.

Recommendations: Taylor Inquiry
1.   We recommend that the Health Authority and Social Services should jointly review to what extent the Trust has now implemented the CPA. We were

told that it has now been fully implemented and we do not suggest that there is any reason to doubt that but we do think the Authority and Social Services should satisfy themselves of that fact. The NHSE CPA monitoring tool may be an appropriate method of examining this.

2.   We recommend that the Trust should make it part of the task of each of its managers to identify whether its staff are carrying into actual effect its basic aims, like providing care in accordance with best practice. Wherever possible any monitoring carried out by managers should have, as a specific object, the identification of success or failure in such areas. Even though monitoring success or failure in these respects is not as easy as in some other aspects of the work of a hospital, because it is not as easily analysed in a statistical fashion, it must be recognised that it is the *raison d'être* of a hospital and must therefore be at the forefront of management's concerns.

3.   We recommend that the Health Authority should set up a formal procedure by which Social Services, the Trust and the Health Authority can monitor the implementation of the Care Programme Approach and any other similar policies which concern all three agencies. Within that procedure there should be a clearly defined process by which each agency can raise matters of concern about such implementation. This procedure should focus on examples of, and the need for, good practice.

4.   We recommend that operational managers should periodically review multi-disciplinary working and circulate their reviews to managers responsible for the other disciplines within the team inviting their comments with a view to sustaining the involvement of those other groups.

5.   We recommend that the Trust should carry out a review of current practice for aftercare planning, to take account of patients' carers and patients as carers with a view to giving more weight to their needs in those contexts. The review could form part of the planning for the implementation of the Carers (Recognition and Services) Act 1995 and would then involve Social Services.

6.   We recommend that a system should be established within the Trust whereby all cases subject to CPA should be raised specifically at a ward round or other multidisciplinary meeting before the patient's discharge and thereafter at suitable intervals (which should be fixed before the patient is discharged) for so long as the patient is subject to the CPA.

7. We recommend that nursing keyworkers should never be appointed from amongst staff who will be absent for any significant part of a patient's stay in hospital and that the appointed keyworker should always be someone who will be on duty for, say, a full shift within the first 24 hours after the patient's admission. We further recommend that the Authority should include this or a similar requirement in its commissioning agreements.

8. We recommend that risk assessment should be specifically mentioned in any forms used as CPA documentation and that the risk assessment should be recorded there.

9. We recommend that if there are any areas of doubt about confidentiality between separate teams looking after patients who are related or one of whom depends upon the other as carer, those doubts should be clarified by the Trust. The Trust and the Authority should carry out a brief exercise to identify any such areas of doubt. Guidance should, in due course, be given to members of staff affected.

10. We recommend that the Trust management should carry out a review of the hospital ward in question to identify any areas where the interactions of staff from different disciplines can be improved and what steps need to be taken to improve those interactions.

11. We recommend that the Trust management should consider whether the location of members of the community mental health team has any adverse consequences for teamwork and generally how teamwork can be improved between the community mental health team and the staff in the ward.

Report of the Inquiry into the Care of Anthony Smith
Professor Sir John Wood (Chair), Mr Malcolm Ashman, Dr Cyril Davies, Dr Huw Lloyd and Mrs Kate Luckett – Southern Derbyshire Health Authority and Derbyshire County Council, October 1996
Synopsis
On 8 August 1995 Anthony Smith killed his mother Gwendoline Smith and his 12-year-old half-brother, David. He pleaded guilty to manslaughter on the grounds of diminished responsibility and received a Section 37/41 under the Mental Health Act 1983. Anthony Smith was born in July 1971. He has no knowledge of his natural father who had already left his mother before his birth. His mother married Peter Smith in 1974, who later adopted Anthony. Anthony's half-sister was born two years later and David was born in 1983. Anthony Smith's childhood and adolescence were unremarkable. His GP first noticed that he had

some emotional problems in May 1994, and referred him for counselling. He was prescribed anti-depressants in September 1994.

In May 1995, he was referred urgently by his GP for a psychiatric opinion. At this stage, when attending his psychiatric outpatient appointment, he told his parents he had a dental appointment. A diagnosis of schizophrenia was made and he was admitted the following day (15 June 1995) to hospital as an informal patient. When discharge was suggested at the end of June, Mr Peter Smith expressed concern to the consultant psychiatrist to the effect that weapons were being hidden and tablets discarded and that he felt his son was causing unrest within the family. 'This was apparently the first and only conversation with AS's relatives' (Smith, 1996, p65). Anthony Smith was discharged to his family on 6 July 1995. He was followed up in the community by a community support nurse. Smith soon began to refuse depot medication, although agreed to take oral medication. He lost his job and isolated himself further from his family. Mrs Smith requested an appointment with the consultant psychiatrist and also with the GP but before she could attend them the tragedy had happened.

Recommendations: Smith Report
Nursing, Medical Assessment and Social Work Involvement
1.   It appears essential that a psychiatric patient with a severe psychiatric illness whose recent history is not known should be assessed by a social worker after admission to hospital and prior to the decision to discharge. Where there appear to be difficulties, an assessment of family or employment circumstances should be made.

Given the psychosocial nature of the impact of schizophrenia, and other severe psychiatric illnesses on the patient, relatives and carers, it is important to ensure that a multidisciplinary and multiagency approach is always adopted.

2.   There should be adequate social work resources available to support the implementation of recommendation 1.

3.   That the role and responsibilities of the 'named nurse' should be reviewed, including the extent of the responsibility to co-ordinate the services given to the patient.

4.   That 'associate nurses' be appointed for each patient so as to ensure continuity of care over the three shifts and during other absences of the 'named nurse'.

5. That the 'named nurse', or an 'associate nurse', should be present at all occasions when decisions are being taken as to the future of the patient. This is especially so with regard to the consideration of a patient at the weekly multidisciplinary meeting. Records of key decisions should be co-ordinated and kept available for consultation by the team of 'named' and 'associate nurses'. Any plan of action should be communicated to those concerned. The responsibilities of the 'named nurse', as set out in the Philosophy of Care for the ward in question, are excellent and should be adhered to.

6. The care plan should specify a programme of activities within the ward programme relevant to the patient's care and to assist rehabilitation.

7. That the 'named nurse' should have a duty to make and maintain contact with the appropriate relatives, friends or carers of the patient so as to form a link with events and opinions of importance to the making of decisions involving the patient.

8. Following leave – weekend or long leave – a clear record of behaviour and incidents at home should be ascertained. Where appropriate, relatives, friends or carers should be interviewed.

9. The co-ordination of the various sources of social work assistance to patients and discharged patients requires careful consideration.

10. All staff should be made aware that crucial information – for example the knowledge of some non-compliance with oral medication and of the interest in and possession of weapons – should be communicated to the multidisciplinary team and to the clinical ward round and a system devised to ensure this takes place. An ongoing assessment of risk should be an integral part of the process.

11. Prior to discharge, a package of care should be arranged to meet the individual's health and social needs.

12. Discharge should include provision for feedback, properly documented to maintain accuracy of information.

13. Where an intended discharge is delayed for further consideration, a full review meeting should be held prior to discharge being granted.

Discharge and Handing Over to Community Care

14. Schizophrenia, defined as a 'severe mental illness', should fulfil the criteria for level II/III of the Care Programme Approach and merit a co-ordinated care package. Within the 'level of need' as identified by the CPA it is recommended that a risk assessment should be included.

15. Nursing documentation should record the discharge process.

16. Action should be taken to ensure greater clarity of responsibility once an in-patient reverts to care in the community.

17. The front-line carer – community support nurse (CSN) or CPN – should have, in addition to the normal process of reporting through his/her seniors, the power to initiate promptly a full review of circumstances that are causing serious concern.

18. The employee specification should set out the competencies required of the post holder and identify the appropriate grade.

19. The delegation of work should follow the appropriate competencies.

20. The quality of the discharge information passed to the community service should be reviewed to ensure that appropriate professional matters are routinely covered.

21. The Consultant should ensure that the patient's GP receives notice of the discharge as soon as possible and his/her medical and social details as necessary to ensure continuity of care.

22. A clinical supervision network should ensure that individual staff are fully supported.

23. The Trust should publish patient information leaflets on medication and ensure this information is promptly communicated to the patient and carers.

24. Patients in the community should not be removed from follow-up, on any grounds, without full consideration of the circumstances involving all the professionals concerned.

25. It is important to strengthen the role of the community link nurse with the ward in question so as to establish continuity of care compatible with the Care Programme Approach.

26. The practice of changing the Community Link Nurse every three months should be reconsidered.

Communications
27. There should be one healthcare record for each patient through all contacts with the Trust.

General Recommendations – Counselling Services

28. The central organisation of all counselling services should be further strengthened so as to support effective use and to co-ordinate appointment and training.

29. The current training should be offered to all counsellors with the purpose of clarifying their role in the care of patients/clients and of ensuring their ability to recognise when there is the need for reference to other specialists. They need to have an understanding of the early symptoms of mental illness.

30. Bearing in mind the variations of counselling practice that currently exist, guidance should be made available to GPs as to the most effective use of the differing forms of counselling.

31. Building on the varying rules and practice of the various professional bodies in counselling, clear rules should be promulgated by the Health Authority, setting out for counsellors the basic standards expected. Clarity of the rules as to the sharing of information is crucially important.

32. Standard requirements, also set out in the job specification, including the duty to attend training and discussion sessions, should also be included in contracts offered to counsellors. The current support for counsellors should be extended to include trainees and qualified counsellors on professional placement.

33. More collaboration would be appropriate between mental health services and primary care counsellors. Counsellors should have a periodic opportunity to discuss their work generally with psychiatrists, GPs and social workers. This might be achieved by an annual study session.

34. Attendance at joint training sessions for general practitioners and practice staff on the use of counsellors should be encouraged.

35. The limits of confidentiality between the various professionals concerned with a patient's care should be carefully defined, indicating the circum stances in which others must be informed.

36. As comprehensive a register of counsellors as possible should be available, setting out the type of counselling they are prepared to offer.

General Recommendations – Assessment and Planning to Meet Social Care Needs

37. The discussions of the patient's progress and problems in the hospital should be given more formality: the philosophy of care and nursing being operated

should be clearly identified and the responsibility for dealing with problems made clear.

38.   Steps should be taken to ensure that at appropriate times patients and their carers are included in discussions concerning discharge and aftercare.

39.   A discharge letter by, or on behalf of, the consultant should deal with social aspects in addition to the strictly medical. It should always be approved by the consultant.

General Recommendations – The Care Programme Approach
40.   Screening for the Care Programme Approach should be ongoing throughout the period as inpatient.

41.   In the case of all patients, a social worker and wherever possible relatives should be involved in this screening.

42.   Schizophrenia, a severe mental illness, should warrant level 2 or level 3 of the Care Programme Approach, thus receiving a multidisciplinary review of need or a co-ordinated care package.

General Recommendations – Inpatient Care
43.   Effective training of the named nurse and the delineation of the duties and responsibilities within the ward philosophy of care are essential.

44.   The nursing handover should explicitly involve the passing on of relevant patient information, which should be documented.

45.   There should be early identification of the particular needs of the patient as an individual, as well as in terms of his/her illness.

46.   The information passed on to those undertaking community care on discharge should be full, as set out in the development model of nursing used in the ward in question.

47.   Firm efforts should be made to devise and supervise an inpatient programme to occupy and assist in the rehabilitation of a patient.

48.   Ward staff should ensure that they are aware of a patient's location at all times during their inpatient stay.

49.   Prior to discharge it is essential to have a co-ordination meeting to assess needs and nominate, as appropriate, a care co-ordinator.

50. The assessment of the home circumstances of patients, particularly those with behavioural problems such as with schizophrenia, should be regarded as essential.

General Recommendations – Treatment and Care in the Community

51. A formal network of clinical supervision should be established and consideration should be given to the recommendations of the Butterworth Report on clinical supervision in nursing.

52. The Community Mental Health Service should receive full professional information from those with medical responsibility for the patient.

53. Allocation of individual patients should take full note of the difficulty of the case and the level of experience of the nurse.

54. Initial home assessment of those diagnosed as suffering from schizophrenia should be made by a Community Psychiatric Nurse.

55. A Community Nurse should be designated, for a period of a year or so, in each of the relevant areas, as a formal link with the ward.

56. After a year has elapsed from the implementation of these recommendations, a review should be undertaken to assess their impact and to give an opportunity to consider any necessary reinforcements of their objectives.

Report of the Independent Inquiry into The Treatment and Care of Richard John Burton
Hugh Chapman (Chair), Malcolm Ashman, Oluwafemi Oyebode and Brian Rogers – Leicestershire Health Authority, October 1996
Synopsis
In May 1995 Richard Burton killed his landlady, Mrs Symons. He subsequently pleaded guilty to manslaughter on the grounds of diminished responsibility and received a hospital order with a restriction order under the Mental Health Act 1983. Richard Burton was born in February 1964, the youngest of three children. Although he began a course at university in 1982, it seems that he felt less able than his siblings, who both went to Oxbridge. He was first admitted to hospital for treatment for depression in his first term at university after the break-up of a relationship with a girlfriend. He returned to his university course in 1984 but remained for only about a month. He moved back to his parents' home in Leicester and later in 1984 was referred to the day hospital in Leicester where a diagnosis of schizoid personality disorder was made.

Subsequently he attended a higher education course at the local polytechnic, which he left after six months. In 1987 while at the polytechnic he was admitted to hospital for psychiatric treatment following an overdose of paracetamol. The diagnosis was depressive personality disorder. During this admission he was interviewed by a student nurse to whom he disclosed fantasies to harm his parents. He was discharged to the day hospital. During this admission to the day hospital, a student social worker completed a social work assessment. Burton subsequently took another overdose and was briefly admitted to hospital but was discharged without further follow-up. He moved into a bed-sit and obtained employment as a hospital porter. He began a long-term relationship in 1988, and in 1990 he and his girlfriend bought a house together.

This relationship broke down in March 1995 and he moved into rented accommodation. In April 1995, he attended his GP's surgery feeling desperate because of the ending of his relationship with his girlfriend six weeks earlier, and was prescribed an anti-depressant. He was seen early in May by the duty doctor at the accident and emergency department, to which he went because he had taken an overdose of 'Lemsip' sachets. The duty doctor arranged for him to be seen as an outpatient by a psychiatrist two weeks later.

The conclusion of this report is that there was no evidence to suggest that Richard Burton was a risk to others and that the killing of Mrs Symons could not reasonably have been predicted or prevented. The recommendations that are made are few and are probably of less significance than those of many other inquiries.

Recommendations: Burton Inquiry

1. Although the absence of some medical and nursing records was not significant for the purposes of the Inquiry, it raised a question about present practices concerning the storage, security, retention, and disposal of such records. It is, therefore, recommended that the Health and Social Services authorities should review their arrangements.

2. Users and carers. Systems and procedures for involving patients and carers in the assessment, planning and delivery of services, particularly around discharge and after-care, should be formalised and published for the guidance of all concerned.

3. The Health Authority, the Trusts and the Social Services Department should review the information they produce to promote interagency working and communication so that it is standardised as far as possible and is clear about team boundaries and contact points.

4.   There also appears to be a need for a directory of support agencies to be available to GPs, clinicians, community team workers, and others which will provide a source of referral for a range of mental health needs.

Report to Northumberland Health Authority of the Independent Inquiry Team into the Care and Treatment of Richard Stoker
Mr A G Brown (Chair), Dr F M Harrop, Mr H J Cronin and Mr J C Harman – Northumberland Health Authority, December 1996
Synopsis
In May 1995 Richard Stoker stabbed and killed Halina Szymczuk, a mental health service user living in the community. He was found guilty of manslaughter on the grounds of diminished responsibility and is detained in a high security hospital. Richard Stoker was born in August 1936. His early childhood was said to have been uneventful apart from difficulties attaining numeracy and literacy skills. He obtained employment after leaving school, but at the age of 19 was convicted of indecent assault on two young girls. As a result of this he was certified as mentally defective and detained for two years in hospital. At the age of 28 he married and later had two daughters. About 10 years later Richard Stoker sustained a head injury and his behaviour changed – he began drinking heavily and accumulating debts.

Against this background, when he was nearly 40, Richard Stoker stabbed and killed his mother-in-law, after being disturbed as he tried to steal money from her house. In 1976, he was convicted of manslaughter on the grounds of diminished responsibility due to mental subnormality; his IQ was assessed as being around 60. After nine years in a special hospital, he was transferred to a medium secure unit, and a year later, in 1986, he was transferred to a locked ward of a local hospital, followed by placement on a rehabilitation ward. In 1987, he obtained a conditional discharge from a Mental Health Review Tribunal, with conditions of medical supervision from his Responsible Medical Officer, social supervision from a probation officer, and residence at a social services hostel for discharged psychiatric patients.

He developed a relationship with a female resident, the couple moved into a flat of their own, and married in 1989. However, problems emerged for both Richard Stoker and his wife. The pressures of independent living were considerable resulting in his wife's readmission to hospital, followed by a further period living together in the community. As arguments and tensions between the couple escalated, Richard Stoker's dependence on alcohol increased, his tendency to self-harm became more noticeable, as did his threatening behaviour towards his wife. This resulted in marital breakdown and the couple separated in 1992. By 1993, his wife no longer wished to see him and Richard Stoker became increasingly distressed. During 1994, his social and financial situation deteriorated further. He was unable to care for himself adequately, living an impoverished and chaotic existence. Unsuccessful attempts were made by his care team to obtain alternative placement for him in a nursing home. It seems that emphasis was placed on keeping him in the community rather than resorting to powers of recall to hospital under the terms of his restriction order. He was unwilling to consider informal admission to hospital. Some of the issues regarding reassessing Richard Stoker's risk are considered in the section dealing with probation (pp 186-7).

Recommendations: Stoker Inquiry

It is our duty to make some recommendations arising out of the Inquiry into this case in the hope that improvements or benefits for the future may arise. Some of our recommendations are, of necessity, of more specific rather than general application and we feel that all agencies should be encouraged to take all of these on board because the number of cases of this kind which each agency will experience will be just a small proportion of their total workload.

The Care Team

1.   Where there is such a case in which a Conditionally Discharged patient with this type of background is placed in the care and management of a multidisciplinary team it is, in our view, important that members of that care team have the training, experience and background which suits them for such a role – and we refer particularly to the training recommendations and requirements for Probation Officers and Community Psychiatric Nurses who have to fill a role in such a care team and the need for the Consultant Psychiatrist to be an appropriately placed and experienced person as referred to below.

2.   Communication and collaboration are, of course, absolutely essential within a care team and indeed there is no need for us to make any recommendation on this – it is already, surely, established practice and case-law – although there were particular issues and deficiencies in this case. We would, therefore, in the light of the circumstances of this case, underline how absolutely essential it is to hold regular case conferences and always to communicate fully. We would add that, although one member of the team (usually the Consultant Psychiatrist) would normally be recognised as the team leader, it must be made absolutely clear that any member of a care team can, and is, entitled to require (and if necessary, in default, convene) a case conference or similar multidisciplinary meeting to ensure there is at all times a co-ordinated approach to care and the regular exchange of views.

Communication

3.   The Trust should establish strict standards for reports, recording letters and other communications to be observed by all of its staff and the implementation of the standards should be regularly reviewed and audited.

4. We consider that the General Practitioner will always have a role to play in the management of a case such as this, and should at the outset be identified and receive regular communication. A patient's General Practitioner should also be invited to contribute to multidisciplinary and CPA meetings and would, we feel sure, have a most useful contribution to make.

Risk Assessment and Risk Management
5. A protocol must be established and implemented to ensure that proper risk assessment and risk management proceedings are fully audited and applied in all relevant cases.

Patient Records
6. We would take the opportunity following the experience of examining records in this case to recommend that inpatient and outpatient records be amalgamated on the same file so that there is a single combined record of a patient always available.

Care Team Membership
7. Whenever there is a change in the employment or role of a member of a care team, this must immediately be reported and considered so that a positive and constructive assessment can be made as to whether that officer ought to continue as a member of the care team or be replaced by another or more appropriate officer. This is not a criticism of the quality and service of the officer who will be replaced but simply designed to ensure that persons in the right disciplines and roles contribute to the care team approach.

8. The above recommendation inevitably brings us to the question of the role of the RMO in this case, in the light of the concerns expressed in evidence to us about her continued role and the transfer of this case which should have occurred but did not. We would recommend, therefore, that, within the limits of clinical independence of Consultants, an employing Trust should see as part of its role as an employer in ensuring that the person in the role of supervising consultant psychiatrist remains appropriate to that role and should assist (and where appropriate insist) in relocation and reprovision of that role in the event of changes occurring. It must be in everyone's interests to ensure that the person in that very important role remains the right and most appropriate one.

9. We consider additionally that the role of the Medical Director of the Trust should be extended/defined as including a specific audit programme of the cases of all Conditional Discharge Patients who are in the care of the Trust, to ensure that all proper procedures and practices in relation to such patients are being followed and audited and the proper management is in place.

Learning Lessons: Report into the events leading to the incident at St John s Way Medical Centre in December 1995
Rosemary Nicholson (Chair), Florence Pevsner, Christina Schwabenland and Cllr Milton Babulall with independent professional advisers: Dr Michael Lowe, Ben Thomas, Dr Malcolm Fox, and David Pope – Camden & Islington Health Authority, December 1996

Synopsis

In December 1995 Maria Caseiro stabbed Dr Inwald, a General Practitioner. The incident was not fatal. But although not mandatory, an independent inquiry was established in order to learn lessons from the incident (Nicholson, 1996, p1.) Eighteen days before the incident Maria Caseiro had been discharged by a Mental Health Review Tribunal from Section 3 of the Mental Health Act 1983. She attended a GP surgery in order to obtain some sleeping tablets, and had apparently taken a knife with her to try to ensure that she obtained what she wanted. The GP summoned assistance from a colleague. Maria Caseiro stabbed the colleague as he tried to restrain her. She was later convicted of unlawful wounding under Section 20 of the Offences Against the Persons' Act and detained under Section 37/41 of the Mental Health Act 1983, under a dual classification of psychopathic disorder and mental illness (depression).

Maria Caseiro was born in November 1966 in Portugal. She reports having experienced a very difficult and disturbed childhood. At the age of 25 she came to Britain. She had a long history of overdoses both before and after her arrival. Her first known contact with mental health services was in 1994 when she was diagnosed as having a borderline personality disorder. This diagnosis was later expanded to include major depression with psychotic features.

Maria Caseiro remained in hospital detained under Section 3 of the MHA 1983 between September 1994 and November 1995. She was transferred between a series of different hospital wards according to her assessed treatment and security needs and resource availability. This led to differing medical views as to her level of risk and whether or not she necessitated continued detention. Maria Caseiro appealed against her detention under Section 3 on two occasions. The Mental Health Review Tribunal on 24 November concluded that in view of the RMO's evidence it 'was obliged to discharge the patient from Section' (Nicholson, 1996, p11). There was confusion as to whether the tribunal could agree to a delayed discharge as recommended by the RMO. The advice from the tribunal clerk was that this was not legally possible. 'A key issue in Maria Caseiro's case is whether delayed discharge was an option to the MHRT' (Nicholson, 1996, p23). This leads directly to recommendation number eight.

Recommendations: Learning Lessons

1. A policy should be agreed on action to be taken where the clinical opinions of the specialist team and the catchment team differ; where there are irreconcilable differences between the consultants, an independent view from a senior consultant should be taken with agreement to abide by the advice and for the *status quo* to remain in the meantime.

2. A protocol for operating the Care Programme Approach (CPA) must be agreed at an early stage between the specialist and catchment area services (involving the local authority social services), recognising that it is a joint responsibility.

3. Where CPA meetings to discuss transfers between units are arranged, the existing and prospective Responsible Medical Officers (RMOs) should be present or represented by someone of sufficient seniority to act on their behalf.

4. There should be formal agreement, copied to all team members, and regular review of the keyworker as the most appropriate person will change during the course of the patient's care plan.

5. Operational policies of specialist units must allow for exceptional circumstances and acknowledge that the RMO's responsibilities extend to ensuring effective transfer to care in the community, where an individual is discharged direct.

6. Operational policies should be reviewed regularly in the light of experience and, as a minimum, every two years.

7. Specialist units have a responsibility to operate a supervision register for the individual patients under their care.

8. The Secretary of State should ask the Mental Health Act Commission to submit proposals, for inclusion in the Code of Practice, for definitive advice on delayed discharge to be given to Mental Health Review Tribunals.

9. As good practice, copies of reports prepared by RMOs in specialist inpatient units for Mental Health Review Tribunals should be sent to the local catchment area consultant in reasonable time prior to the hearing in order to allow the local consultant to make his or her opinion known.

10. The Lord Chancellor should ensure that Mental Health Review Tribunals participate fully in inquiries, set up as a result of HSG (94) 27, into homicides, suicides and other serious incidents.

11. As good practice, keyworkers should take responsibility for ensuring that care is co-ordinated and that all those with a potential for providing care are kept informed, including the GP and the local psychiatric services.

12. All staff who may be required to act as keyworkers should have a clear understanding of the Care Programme Approach and receive regular refresher training on a joint basis as a matter of good practice.

13. The Health Authority should assess with the Local Medical Committee (LMC) and the postgraduate tutors whether GP awareness of the Care Programme Approach needs to be raised and take any necessary action.

14. When a patient without a GP leaves hospital after a CPA, it is good practice for the keyworker to encourage the patient to register with a local GP.

15. Both the keyworker and the RMO have a responsibility to ensure that the GP, once known, is briefed at an early stage, with a prompt discharge summary on the case from the RMO.

16. Practices should have clear policies for the registration of new patients and for dealing with patients who may pose a problem for staff.

17. All front-line staff should have received training, preferably in their work-place, in how to manage individuals who may be disturbed, aggressive, troubled or distressed.

18. All practices should review their premises to ensure that they meet Health and Safety regulations and offer reasonable levels of security for staff in terms of layout and ability to summon assistance, taking account of the characteristics of their practice population.

19. The Health Authority jointly with the LMC should agree good practice guidance on levels of security including layout of consulting rooms, the ability to summon assistance, and appropriate levels of staffing.

20. The Health Authority and LMC should agree a policy on their respective contributions in providing support to practices in the event of traumatic incidents such as this, in order to ensure that staff receive appropriate counselling and advice and that services for practice patients are maintained.

21. The Health Authority should satisfy itself that the Care Programme Approach is being applied consistently and appropriately for its residents;

by using the audit tool developed by the Royal College of Psychiatrists and issued with circular HSG (96) 6.

22.   The Health Authority with the Local Authorities should ensure that staff with key roles in implementing the Care Programme Approach are trained in a joint and integrated way.

23.   The Health Authority should ensure that appropriate arrangements and responsibilities are clearly agreed for the Care Programme Approach between the local service and providers outside the district, whether NHS or not.

24.   The Health Authority should ensure that, in planning the future pattern of service, the level of need is assessed and account is taken of the accessibility, quality and compatibility of all elements of a comprehensive service.

25.   In the light of the Panel's findings, the Boards of the two NHS Trusts and Social Services Committee of Islington Council review their internal arrangements for investigations into serious incidents to ensure that they are satisfactory.

26.   The Boards of the two NHS Trusts and Social Services Committee review their own findings in the light of the Panel's report and agree what further action is now required.

27.   The Health Authority should satisfy itself that investigations by providers into serious incidents involving its residents are sufficiently critical to ensure that appropriate lessons are learnt.

28.   The Health Authority, West London Healthcare NHS Trust, Camden & Islington Community Health Services NHS Trust and the London Borough of Islington should each prepare action plans in response to the report within three months.

The Report into the Care and Treatment of Martin Mursell
Mr Lincoln Crawford (Chair), Mr J. E. Devaux, Dr Robert Ferris and Mrs Patricia Hayward – Camden & Islington Health Authority, March 1997

Synopsis
In October 1994 Martin Mursell stabbed and killed Joe Collins, his stepfather, and attempted to kill his mother, Mary Collins. He pleaded guilty to the murder of Joe Collins and the attempted murder of Mary Collins and was sentenced to life and 10 years' imprisonment to run concurrently. He is now detained in a high secure hospital. Martin Mursell was born in May 1967. His life appears to have been uneventful until late adolescence, when his mental state started to deteriorate. He also abused alcohol and drugs from about the age of 16. However, although his

family were concerned and he expressed fears about paranoid thoughts and feelings, he refused to see a doctor. When he was 21, he was convicted of a serious assault (ABH) on his girlfriend, which occurred because he suspected his girlfriend was having an affair. Martin Mursell's behaviour became increasingly bizarre and frightening with the result that, by 1989, when he was 21, he was admitted to hospital under Section 2 MHA 1983 following a request for help from his mother. A diagnosis of schizophrenia was made. Martin Mursell received care and treatment from mental health services for almost five years before the attack on his mother and stepfather. During this time his care and treatment were variable in their quality and consistency.

A cycle of five more hospital admissions occurred with some response to inpatient treatment, discharge, relapse, and readmission. Housing was a particularly contentious and sensitive issue for Martin Mursell. He wanted to live independently, but his illness made it difficult for him to manage and the housing department was not always willing or able to help him. The outcome of unsatisfactory housing for Martin Mursell was that he often returned to his mother's home, which exacerbated his problems and also increased the risks, or he was placed in bed and breakfast accommodation. By 1990 the risk posed to Mrs Mursell by her son threatening violence towards her was clear, although it was not formally assessed. Martin Mursell presented many challenges to the mental health professionals involved in his care, not least because of his reluctance to comply with medication. However, the report concludes that Martin Mursell's stability in the community was compromised further at times when services were fragmented and were not offering co-ordinated or consistent care.

Martin Mursell's last admission to hospital was the first that did not require his compulsory detention. However, when he was discharged for the last time in August 1994, once again it was to bed and breakfast accommodation, despite the fact that it was inappropriate to meet his needs. Loss of contact with services for nearly three months was considered to be a likely contributory factor to his relapse and subsequent events. 'The care which Martin received in the community fell short of what was needed to such an extent that it became more likely that a serious incident would occur' (Mursell, 1997, p85).

Recommendations: Mursell Report
Housing
1. We recommend that an officer of appropriate seniority be appointed to ensure that there is effective co-ordination in mental health cases between Health, Housing and Social Services.

2.   We recommend that the existing practice of monthly 'callovers' whereby a member of the Mental Health Social Work Team meets with the Housing Client and Contract Manager to review mental health cases on the Neighbourhood housing list be immediately adopted as a formal procedure between Health, Housing and Social Services and appropriate guidelines be developed.

3.   We recommend that, as part of a regular monitoring exercise, housing officers report to the housing committee at each cycle, on all decisions taken on mental health cases.

4.   We recommend that the Secretary of State should consider amending the current guidelines for local authorities when dealing with homelessness, to ensure that mentally ill people are not required to pass through unsuitable transitional accommodation, for example bed-and-breakfast accommodation, before being furnished with permanent accommodation for their needs.

Social Services
5.   We recommend that a directory should be kept which details the expertise of all prospective supervisors, and before such individuals are asked to supervise inexperienced social workers, the person making that decision must ensure that the proposed supervisor has the required skills and expertise.

6.   We recommend that where a social worker is the keyworker in an aftercare plan, immediate notice must be given to the team manager if there is a breakdown in the plan, setting out the full reason for the breakdown. This should be in addition to the social worker's responsibility to the rest of the multidisciplinary team.

7.   We recommend that the Borough makes provision for induction training of officers at all levels from Housing and Social Services, to ensure that there is familiarisation with, and a better grasp of, the policy and practice of each others' responsibilities.

       We recommend that before a case is transferred to the duty system a detailed risk assessment should be undertaken and recorded. The decision to transfer the case should then be communicated to the client in writing and to the team manager.

8.   We recommend that all duty social workers should have some basic awareness in mental health work and should have ready access to an ASW for advice.

Health

9.   Some confusion is caused when the word 'discharge' is used in different contexts. We recommend that the Trust should use the words 'release from section' instead of 'discharge from section'.

10. Where a mentally ill patient has a past history of violence to others, we recommend that a risk assessment must be carried out by the Trust and recorded prior to discharge, regardless of the presence or absence of other variables such as drug misuse and non-compliance.

11. We recommend that the Trust and the borough meet urgently to consider whether the introduction of the CPA will also ensure a single care plan for all clients of the mental health services.

12. We recommend that where a patient is transferred from one hospital to another within the Trust before his or her care plan becomes operational, the plan must also be transferred with the patient and should be taken into account when a fresh plan is being devised. All the casenotes in total must always accompany a patient who moves within the Trust to ensure continuity of care.

13. The Trust and the Local Authority should ensure that all professionals concerned with the discharge of a patient are familiar with the requirements of Section 117 of the MHA and any supporting local or national guidelines. We therefore recommend that the Trust and the Social Services urgently set up a working party to consider the best way of delivering and updating training in Section 117 procedures and ensuring compatibility with CPA training. We suggest that the training be given in the following areas:–

     (a)   The requirements of Section 117 MHA and the national and local guidelines on this procedure;

     (b)   the role of each professional involved; and

     (c)   how such meetings should be conducted.

14. We recommend that where there is evidence of poor or non-compliance with treatment or persistent failure to keep outpatient appointments, the keyworker should bring this to the attention of the multidisciplinary team who devised the original plan, and a clear strategy worked out to try and improve compliance.

15. We recommend that the boundaries between the duties of a community psychiatric nurse and a community mental health worker can be clarified by the Trust and other professionals informed.

16. We recommend that immediate steps be taken to improve the standard of record keeping at the Unit concerned and in the community mental health services.

The Law Society
17. We recommend that the Law Society should now give consideration to including mental health awareness training for solicitors as part of its continuing education programme.

Carers and Users
18. We recommend that the Trust and the Health Authority ensure that provision is made for carers to have respite breaks.

19. We recommend that the Trust ensures that all aftercare plans include a consideration of the patient's employment opportunities and leisure activities, with the aim of removing him or her away from dependency on the carer.

20. We recommend that the Trust makes arrangements so far as is practicable for carers to be involved in the aftercare process on an equal footing with professionals. We also recommend that the Trust ensures that information shared by professionals must also be shared with the carer, subject to the user's consent.

21. We recommend that the Trust and the Local Authority ensure that the patient's keyworker is involved at all times with the carer.

Agencies Working Together
22. We recommend that Health, Housing and Social Services should work together to develop a strategic approach to accommodation for mentally ill people and that the co-ordination of service provision be monitored regularly.

23. We recommend that Health and Social Services and purchasers and providers agree the essential requirements of service and, ensure that proper arrangements are made so that contract monitoring and any audit will readily indicate the degree of effectiveness of the services delivered.

The Trust and Social Services
24. Are invited to consider drawing up an agreed joint management structure for community mental health services with a jointly appointed officer to ensure that planned services are not only relevant but also delivered. Joint monitoring arrangements should be put in place at the same time to ensure that the service is actually delivered.

Mental Health Act Commission

25. We recommend that the Secretary of State for Health should consider extending the remit of the Mental Health Act Commission so as to enable it to ensure that:–

   (i)   the new powers of Supervised Discharge are correctly exercised and applied strictly in accordance with the statutory requirements;

   (ii)   by a process of observation and monitoring over a number of years, the use of the powers is of benefit to the patients involved and to the community into which the patients have been discharged.

Training

26. We recommend that:–

   (a)   all professional staff should be afforded the opportunity to obtain a post basic qualification in their chosen speciality;

   (b)   staff with basic qualifications must receive regular supervision from senior staff who are qualified to practise in contemporary mental health services;

   (c)   staff without post basic qualification in mental health care should not work with people on level 3 CPA unless supervised by a suitably qualified senior.

Chapter 3
Implications and Issues

Risk Assessment and Management

Being able to assess risk and then to manage it successfully is fundamental to community care.

'Risk Assessment is the method and procedure by which the risks perceived to attend a given situation, a given set of facts, or some proposed course of conduct in connection with these are considered, measured, assessed and recorded, so that the appropriateness of a present situation or a proposed course of conduct can be the better measured and determined' (Stoker, 1996, p28). This statement comes from the report of the inquiry into care and treatment of Richard Stoker published in December 1996. Risk assessment and management are now a central issue in mental health inquiry reports.

One of the stated aims of public inquiries is that this source material should inform service delivery and should be used constructively to improve services for the mentally ill. As early as 1992, for example, the Rooney Inquiry team stated their terms of reference as being to 'report their findings and to recommend any action which, in the light of these, might assist the assessment and care of mentally disabled patients and the public from the protection of those patients and the risk of harm' (Rooney, 1992, p2). The 1994 guidance has resulted in inquiry reports addressing risk assessment within their terms of reference (NHSE, 1994). One way for mental health professionals to improve their skills in assessing risk and managing it is by integrating into their practice the crucial lessons that are becoming increasingly apparent in the light of the many inquiries of the 1990s.

Included in the terms of reference of the Clunis Inquiry is the remit to 'make recommendations for the future delivery of care including admission, treatment, discharge and continuing care to people in similar circumstances so that, as far as possible, harm to patients and the public is avoided' (Clunis, 1994, p1.) All practitioners have been influenced to change their practice to a greater or lesser extent by the Clunis recommendations. They remain important in informing best practice particularly in risk assessment. Examples of inquiry reports which are explicit about investigating the quality of the risk assessment include the Robinson Inquiry (Blom-Cooper, 1995), Woodley (1995), Grey (1995), Viner (1996), Hampshire (1996), and Stoker (1996). Thus, in the case of Robinson, it articulates that it will 'consider the lessons and implications arising' (Blom-Cooper, 1995, p9) and goes on to say that 'the risk which Andrew Robinson posed to other people during the course of his illness was naturally a major focus of our inquiry' (Blom-Cooper, 1995, p175).

One example of a report which emphasises risk assessment in its terms of reference is the Viner Report (1996), although there are many more. The components of Viner's terms of reference include *inter alia*:

1. To examine all the circumstances surrounding the treatment and care of Mr Robert Viner by the Mental Health and Social Services, in particular: *the quality and scope of his health and social care and risk assessments*, the suitability of his treatment, care and supervision in respect of:

    ● his assessed health and social care needs

    ● his assessed risk of potential harm to himself or others

    ● any previous psychiatric history

    ● the number and nature of any previous court convictions.

2. To consider the adequacy of the training in the assessment of risk of all the mental health care staff involved in Mr Viner's care (Viner, 1996, p91; emphasis added).

Four major issues recur in the reports, which are considered below. The first is *thoroughness*. Attention to detail, accurate and detailed recording, and comprehensive history-taking remain fundamental to an effective understanding of someone's risk. Linked to this is the importance of not minimising incidents and not responding to each one individually which of course requires both a historical as well as an immediate perspective to be taken. Treating incidents of violence separately may lead to a pattern of escalating dangerousness being overlooked and will result in unacceptable levels of risk. Second, real *team working* is crucial, including proper interagency co-operation, effective liaison and not hiding behind confidentiality. Third, involving and listening to all members of the *clinical team* including more-junior staff members is not a luxury but a necessity. Finally, fourth, it is crucial to listen to carers and relatives as well as the service user so that their working alliance with the professional team is a truly therapeutic one.

There are times when this level of thoroughness, co-operation and team-working will be difficult and it will seem easier to avoid facing painful situations. It may seem simpler to argue, for example, that the service user's right to confidentiality means that seeking out the views and feelings of immediate family members can be sidestepped. It is important to re-evaluate the concept of confidentiality. Practitioners must feel more confident about 'asking the unaskable' (Prins, 1995, p242), and recognise the responsibility that professionals must accept in this difficult culture of community care for the mentally disordered offender, balancing the rights of the community to be safe while not riding roughshod over civil liberties.

Thoroughness
The need for detailed information and accurate data as a prerequisite for the starting point of any risk assessment is widely acknowledged. However, the inquiries into situations that have resulted in disastrous outcomes highlight this fact very powerfully. So, for example, the Clunis Inquiry makes three specific recommendations in relation to risk assessment:

(i)   An accurate record should be made of any incident of violence and the details should be included in the patient's discharge summary

(ii) An assessment of the risk of dangerousness should be included in the discharge summary whenever the patient has acted with violence

(iii) Everyone who has contact in his professional or service work with mentally ill people who may pose a risk of violence should have training in the assessment of dangerousness, and understand when to refer the patient for expert guidance
(Clunis, 1994, p119).

The Clunis Inquiry also quoted Dr Nigel Eastman as saying that 'the only decent predictor of future behaviour is past behaviour' (Clunis, 1994, p118). Yet despite the fact that this principle is widely acknowledged as fundamental to an accurate assessment of risk, the Clunis Inquiry team was critical of the way in which, in the case of Christopher Clunis, violent incidents were treated in isolation from each other and were not seen as forming part of a developing history of serious aggressive and dangerous behaviour. Not only was the pattern of such incidents overlooked but also it was discovered that there was a tendency to minimise the seriousness of individual threats and acts of violent behaviour.

The much repeated statement 'nothing predicts behaviour like behaviour' features in several other reports. Probably the most notable is the Kirkman inquiry (1991), which is still often quoted with reference to risk assessment. The inquiry team investigating the case of Kim Kirkman considered that the following eight factors each play a part in making a judgement about risk to others:

●   The past history of the patient.

●   Self-reporting by the patient at interview.

●   Observation by trained staff of both the behaviour and mental state of the patient.

- Discrepancies between what is reported and what is observed.

- Some physiological tests such as the polygraph and the penile plethysmograph

- Psychological testing including inventory techniques for measuring personality traits and the Semantic Differential for shifts in conceptual thinking.

- Statistics derived from studies of related cases.

- Prediction indicators derived from research. (Kirkman, 1991, pp15-16).

An illustration of the importance of obtaining adequate information in order to assess risk accurately can be seen in the Boland Inquiry (1995). This inquiry investigates the circumstances which led to the deaths of Alan Boland and his mother, Ellen. Alan Boland had received psychiatric outpatient treatment for nine years before he killed his 71-year- old mother with whom he shared a flat. The first and only detailed case history taken at the time of the original referral identified 'a lot of psychopathology in the relationship with his mother, dating from early childhood' (Boland, 1995 p7), although it was not until two months before Mrs Boland's death that it was recorded that Mr Boland had been illegitimate and that his birth had been kept secret from his relatives. Without information from Mrs Boland during his nine years of treatment an understanding of Mr Boland's situation and psychosocial problems would of necessity be incomplete. The inquiry team considered that in the absence of adequate information, Mr Boland's difficulties were underestimated' (Boland, 1995, p15).

It is argued, for example in the Woodley Report, that psychiatrists do not assess violent behaviour or the possibility of violent behaviour routinely as they would assess the risk of suicide (Woodley, 1995, p105). One of the lessons in improving the quality of risk assessment from a great number of the inquiries (for example, Woodley, Boland, Burton, and Mitchell) is to recognise the importance of asking about the history of violence and the factors which might trigger it in the future as well as other more commonly assessed factors.

Communication and Liaison
The report investigating the deaths of Alan and Ellen Boland is also a good example of the next important factor emerging from several reports: communication and liaison. The need to work together both within one's own profession and with others is clearly indicated. After the initial assessment interview in 1985 Mr Boland 'was seen on frequent occasions over the next nine years by some twenty junior doctors whose letters to the General Practitioner consisted largely of

descriptions of Mr Boland's degree of depression and consumption of alcohol with advice confined to the dosage and form of antidepressants prescribed for his patient (Boland, 1995, p11).

The lack of continuity caused by the sheer number of junior doctors who saw Mr Boland must militate against the development of a trusting relationship and is therefore not conducive to accurate risk assessment.

An additional flaw which hindered procuring sufficient information with which to make any attempt at devising a realistic strategy to either assess or manage the risk concerns the fact that there was no referral to social services for assessment. One of the concerns highlighted by the inquiry team was that 'the medical profession may be acting as "gate keepers" in restricting access to the social services, even for assessment, to cases identified as very severely mentally ill' (Boland, 1995, p13).

Good risk assessment requires different professionals to work together and to share information. In the case of Alan Boland there was no multidisciplinary team operating nor any liaison with other agencies (for example, the Probation Service was not contacted while Mr Boland was on probation for offences of assault and robbery). One of the reports which places particular emphasis on the consequences of the absence of a multiprofessional risk assessment is the Stoker Report. The fact that each discipline involved had considered the risks from its own perspective was inadequate because the information and individual assessments of risk were not shared (Stoker, pp28-29, 1996).

Similarly, the Woodley Report explains vividly why it is so crucial to disclose information to other agencies such as housing associations and day centres on a need-to-know basis (Woodley, 1995). Both the Clunis Inquiry and the Newby Report show how hostels are unable to manage risk safely because the risk is not disclosed to staff at the time of referral for fear of the applicant being rejected. This cannot be right and can have disastrous consequences. In the words of Shepherd, 'professionals cannot hide behind confidentiality as an excuse for poor communication' (Shepherd, 1995, p122).

It is now a familiar finding that, when liaison is poor and that working together both within multidisciplinary teams and across agencies is fragmented and unsatisfactory, the outcome is tragedy. However, it is one thing knowing this and another getting it right. Many of the other inquiries have identified poor communication as a recurring feature, for example Clunis, Sinclair, Newby, Woodley, Grey, Viner, Hampshire, Smith, Mursell and others have all referred to this as a major weakness leading to inadequate risk assessments. In the words of the Smith

Inquiry: 'Given the psycho-social nature of the impact of schizophrenia, and other severe psychiatric illnesses on the patient, relatives and carers, it is important to ensure that a multi-disciplinary and multi-agency approach is always adopted' (Smith, 1996, p21). On a similar note the conclusion to the Viner Report states that '. . . the professional work undertaken with Robert Viner was sometimes impeded by ineffective multidisciplinary team working. . .' (Viner, 1996, p75). The report adds: 'There was, however, little evidence that the teams actually functioned as teams . . . Multidisciplinary working can be problematic, particularly where the team formation takes place in the context of professional rather than functional management' (Viner, 1996, p72).

The fundamental principle of teams working together despite the very real difficulties this seems to cause people is reinforced throughout inquiries and accompanying literature.

> It has to be acknowledged that it is difficult to get teams to work effectively, but unfortunately there is no other solution. The care of individuals with serious mental illness and a potential for serious violence is simply too complicated to be carried by one individual. Effective teamwork is the only means whereby the range of necessary skills to address the problems can be brought together. (Shepherd, 1995, pp122-3.)

Listening to All Members of the Clinical Team
Another of the lessons repeatedly identified by inquiries is that of recognising and valuing the contribution of all staff who are in contact with the patient, especially the most junior team members. One example is the inquiry into the care of Richard Burton (Burton, 1996). Mr Burton was a young man living in Leicester who had received care and treatment for his mental health problems for 12 years before he committed what is known as his 'index offence', i.e. the homicide which has led to the inquiry. He had been assessed as being a risk to himself having taken several overdoses during this time. However, he had never been considered a risk to other people. Yet he killed his landlady. This followed the breakup of his only long term relationship with a girlfriend and a self-referral for renewed psychiatric help. During the inquiry it transpired that, eight years previously, Mr Burton had revealed to a student nurse that he had fantasies to harm his parents. This information was documented and communicated to the supervising nurse but not to the medical staff. Following the homicide Mr Burton disclosed to forensic psychiatrists that his urges to harm his landlady had been present for at least three weeks before the incident and that he had engaged in violent fantasies since early adult life. Subsequently it became known that he had been violent towards his ex-girlfriend on three occasions. Also Mr Burton's mother told the inquiry that in 1987

she had found her son 'holding a knife out towards her' (Burton 1996, p11). This inquiry highlights the fact that information from the student nurse was not fed back to the doctors. Such information may not have prevented the tragedy but clearly, without it, an assessment of risk is incomplete.

Further evidence of the crucial value of the evidence of all team members is shown in the Jason Mitchell Inquiry (Blom-Cooper, 1996). This report is particularly critical of the fact that the detailed report identifying Jason Mitchell's sadistic fantasies, compiled by an occupational therapy technician, was undervalued by the clinical team because of the relatively low status of the clinician.

> Jason Mitchell's case illustrates how contributions from an unqualified member of staff were disregarded, and consequently how important data were put out of sight and mind. Nothing that is relevant to the assessment and treatment of a patient should be ignored, whatever its origins (Blom-Cooper, 1996, p63.)

The Sinclair Inquiry demonstrates that the hospital team did not consider Sinclair's condition as serious or threatening despite a contrary view expressed by the community psychiatric nurse (CPN), thus undermining the confidence in her own judgement of the relatively inexperienced and unsupervised CPN (Sinclair, 1996). In the case of Grey, he killed his mother after going absent without leave immediately following the transfer from a secure to an open hospital ward. There was a discrepancy between the Approved Social Worker's assessment of Grey's family circumstances and that of the ward-based staff. Not surprisingly the inquiry team suggest this lack of clarity contributed to lack of a thorough risk assessment (Grey, 1995).

Listening to Those Closest to the Patient
The fact that a significant proportion of the victims of the recent so-called 'community care' tragedies are close relatives, most often the person's mother, in itself warrants further examination to show what information can be learnt. There are many examples. Boland (1995), Viner (1996) and Kopernik-Steckel (1997) killed their mothers and also themselves. In many cases the relative was also the carer (Smith, 1996 and Sinclair, 1996) but for others (Grey, 1995 and Mursell, 1997) this had become no longer possible because of a history of relationship tensions and in some cases previous threats of violence to the relative. Mitchell (Blom-Cooper, 1996) who had an uneasy relationship with his father killed him. Taylor (1996) was struggling to care for his father who was suffering from dementia, which exacerbated his own mental health problems. Tragically the burden on Keith Taylor, the carer, became too great, culminating in the death of his father. Hampshire (1996) killed his wife who was also his carer.

Robert Viner, at the age of 42, killed his 76-year-old mother with whom he had lived for nearly 20 years, before killing himself. He was 18 when he was first seen by a psychiatrist. He then had intermittent contact with mental health services for the next 24 years, mostly on an outpatient basis, although this included two brief hospital admissions. For the most part he lived with and was cared for by his mother. The report comments that 'until April 1995 the pattern of his life in the community appeared unexceptional, for example he had no history of any sort of offending' (Viner, 1996, p15).

Despite ongoing psychiatric treatment for Mr Viner over many years, Mrs Viner's own needs were largely overlooked. The burden of being the sole carer with inadequate support culminated in her death when the problems became overwhelming. Following this tragedy local policy and practice have altered so that the assessment of risk to the carer is considered much more carefully. One of the difficulties in the case of Robert Viner was that he would not allow his mother to speak to professionals alone when they came to the house to visit him.

> All carers should be given the opportunity to talk in confidence about their own needs. If appropriate, they should be offered a separate assessment, carried out away from the person for whom they provide the care. Despite the indications given by Muriel Viner, there was no effective focus on her needs and her problems. (Viner, 1996, pp50-51.)

This right of the carer to his or her own independent assessment of need has now been enshrined in the recent carer's legislation (Carers [Recognition and Services] Act 1995). In Francis Hampshire's case, both Mr and Mrs Hampshire were in their 60s and had been married for nearly 40 years. Mr Hampshire had been receiving psychiatric care on and off for the previous nine years from the local psychiatric hospital. Again, Mrs Hampshire did not feel able to ask for help for herself because her husband's paranoid belief system was such that it precluded any alliance she may have wanted with professionals. Nevertheless, she gave many messages that all was far from well. Additionally, Mr Hampshire had assaulted his wife previously in the context of his mental illness but the risk that this indicated was never properly examined. 'Mrs Hampshire should not have been left in such a position. She was having to provide round the clock care to a clearly sick husband without any respite or support' [other than when the community nurse visited]. (Hampshire, 1996, p52.)

The Hampshire inquiry provides a very clear example of what can go wrong when the patient is allowed to control the clinical team's intervention, referred to in this report as Mr Hampshire being allowed to 'call the tune' (Hampshire, 1996, p25 and *passim*). Both his wife and the clinicians involved in his care were afraid of upsetting him and exacerbating his irritability with the result that the risk management strategy was described as a 'wait and see policy', which ultimately had disastrous results (Hampshire, 1996, p20 and *passim*). This was a man well known for many years to local psychiatric services. Prior to the index offence the risks were indeed escalating but as Mr Hampshire's mental health deteriorated so his reluctance to accept help and his lack of insight became greater. The inquiry team consider that the following should have been assessed:

- The risk to Frank Hampshire of self-harm due to his deteriorating mental state.

- The risk to Mrs Hampshire inherent in leaving him in her sole care when she had been the victim of an assault by him in a situation of deteriorating mental health.

- The risk of his health deteriorating further without treatment.

- The risk that he would neither take prescribed medication nor attend outpatient appointments.

- The risk that he would refuse any continuation of the services of the Community Psychiatric Nurse.

- The risk that Mrs Hampshire's support would be lost or the burden of care become too great.

- The risk to Mrs Hampshire's own health from the burden of care. (Hampshire, 1996, p51)

One of the major weaknesses in the treatment of Mr Hampshire was the reluctance or inability on the part of the clinical team to include Mrs Hampshire in the therapeutic alliance. This would have provided the team with a vital source of information to help them arrive at an understanding of the risks. To improve the accuracy of risk assessments practitioners must address the issue of involving close relatives and carers in understanding a person's mental illness. It is time to look again at any tendency to hide behind a misguided belief in confidentiality. Payne shows that a concern for confidentiality has to be balanced by an understanding of the implications and value in defined circumstances of openness (Payne, 1996).

In the past, efforts to empower service users have led to reducing the role and importance of significant others. Anthony Smith, the 24-year-old who killed his mother and 12-year-old stepbrother a month after his discharge from a psychiatric hospital, had not wanted his family's views sought by the clinical team. So, on the grounds that he was an adult and therefore had the right to withhold his consent, his parents were not consulted and he was discharged to their care. 'The current importance given to confidentiality' was considered one of the factors that adversely influenced professional practice (Smith, 1996, p19). As a consequence of this practice the Smith Inquiry recommends that whenever someone is admitted to hospital suffering from a severe mental illness and whose history is not known, a social work assessment should be completed before the patient is discharged from hospital (Smith, 1996, rec 1).

Likewise, after Raymond Sinclair killed his 64-year-old mother, the inquiry investigating the circumstances against which the homicide took place indicated that the family's perspective was largely ignored by almost all of the professionals involved. There were many other shortcomings in the delivery of care that in combination produced poor practice, but no real attempt was made to uncover the family's distress prior to the index offence (Sinclair, 1996). This leads the inquiry team to recommend that

> the information and social histories gathered following admission should always consider the views of other family members, carers and other persons close to the patient. Their views should also be sought when Care Programme Approach plans are made before discharge and when they are reviewed after discharge. The only exception should be when the patient has made a formal declaration of unwillingness for them to be involved. (Sinclair, 1996, p64.)

The issues of consent and confidentiality need to be addressed very carefully if we are to make any real progress with these particular elements of risk assessment.

Even where the relative was not the victim, inquiry reports often draw attention to the value which would have been gained in risk assessments from careful attention to the experience and understanding of relatives. The Clunis Inquiry, for example, is critical of the fact that Clunis's sister was never contacted by any of the clinicians involved in his treatment, despite her continuing concern for her brother over a number of years (Clunis, 1994, p8 and *passim*).

Similarly in the Robinson Inquiry (Blom-Cooper, 1995), Andrew Robinson's parents repeatedly tried to convey their concern about their son's dangerousness to the professionals involved. However, in this case the feelings and views of relatives were not seen to carry the same value or objectivity as those of the clinicians. It is most important to understand the patient's view of the world, and to recognise that 'professionals need to be trained to trust the experienced judgement of close family, rather than rely on their own impressions made at one isolated assessment' (Blom-Cooper, 1995, p147).

Effective risk management requires a recognition of the need and right for relatives who are often also the main carers to be involved in care and treatment plans.

> In those very common circumstances where the patient is receiving substantial emotional and practical support from relatives, they surely have a right to know sufficient details about the mental disorder, its likely course, warning symptoms of relapse and how and when to summon help, to enable them to discharge their responsibilities effectively. The key task in working with relatives is to engage them in the overall care plan so that they become partners with the clinical team in their relative's care. (Blom-Cooper, 1995, p147.)

The issue of not understanding the risk by not listening to relatives and carers is such a strong feature of inquiry reports that examples are almost too numerous to mention. In the inquiry into the care and treatment of NG it was established that Mr G's father and brother expressed grave concern about NG's imminent discharge from hospital saying that 'such an action would be the responsibility of others; if discharged as he then was he was likely to kill himself *or* somebody else' (NG, 1996, p13). It appears that the family's views were not taken seriously by the professionals, with tragic consequences. A few months later NG ran over and killed a stranger in a car park.

Blom-Cooper makes a similar point in his analysis of the dysfunctional family dynamics in the case of Mitchell. He considers a more proactive approach to have been indicated when Jason Mitchell wanted to return to his home area, but did not want professionals to make any contact with his father.

> The degree of respect to be paid to patient's choice is always a fine balance. The need to subordinate patient choice, when risk to self or others is in issue, was not called into question in this case. It should have been more actively canvassed by those involved in the discharge of Jason Mitchell to his home environment. (Blom-Cooper, 1996, p186.)

Summary
The essential ingredients of risk assessment are already well documented but inquiries into what has gone wrong refocus existing knowledge and reinforce basic principles in a stark and often salutary way. This more systematic analysis of the content of inquiries which have looked at risk assessment offers a practice-focused approach to enhancing our skills in risk assessment. The cumulative

findings that emerge from the reports so far indicate that there are no short cuts to risk assessment. Thoroughness underpins all qualitative risk management.

According to the Sinclair Inquiry:
> Both recent research findings and properly deployed intuition enable clinicians to go well beyond the limitations of the oft repeated adage "nothing predicts violence like previous violence". But neither information from research nor intuition can be of value in the absence of *an accurate and comprehensive history*, drawing on all sources of available information, and evaluated by an experienced professional. *This is the key to the effective management of dangerous and potentially dangerous behaviour.* (Sinclair, 1996, p66; emphasis added.)

Adrian Grounds considers that risk assessment must be grounded in history: 'the purpose of the history is to identify the possible situations of risk in the future' (Grounds, 1995, p54).

In the words of 'Building Bridges':
> The key principle of risk assessment is to use all available sources of information – a proper assessment cannot be made in the absence of information about a patient's background, present mental state and social functioning, and also his or her past behaviour. As well as the treatment team and the patient, sources may include relatives, carers, friends, the police, probation officers, housing departments, and social workers, and also local press reports and concerns expressed by neighbours. (Department of Health, 1995, p88.)

The fundamental key, judging from the inquiries to date, may be the involvement of not only the patient but also, and crucially, the whole network of people around the patient, not least close relatives and carers as well as all mental health workers engaged in a particular person's care. The Smith Report considers that the medical treatment of Anthony Smith was satisfactory, but observed that there was a 'failure to recognise fully the social aspects of Anthony Smith's problems, that proved to be one of the most important and unfortunate aspects of his care' (Smith, 1996, p19).

All of this has resource implications. Good liaison, for example, is time intensive. Thoroughness, attention to detail, accurate and careful recording, and so on all involve time, and time means resources. 'The idea that thorough risk assessment can be introduced without resource implications because it is only a matter of formalising good practice is a nonsense which takes no account of the reality of the pressures on our services.' (Grounds, 1995, p51.) However, resources alone will not necessarily achieve the desired change, without the commitment to change procedures and practice. This point is made forcibly by the Kopernik- Steckel Inquiry, ' . . . the failings were primarily about procedures, professional practice and communications. Unless these basic problems are addressed by management at all levels, we can have no confidence that an allocation of additional resources would, of itself, prevent a further tragedy' (Kopernik-Steckel, 1997, para. 6.0.9).

A final point to note, especially for managers, relates to the importance of training. All the reports without exception stress the necessity for training in risk assessment as underpinning any strategy to improve the accuracy and quality of the mental health practitioner's skills in assessing risk.

Inquiries, Race, Ethnicity and Cultural Sensitivity
Introduction
The over-representation of black people in the mental health system is well documented and this statistic is reflected in the proportion of the 28 inquiry reports in this study that are concerned with black/ethnic minority mentally disordered offenders. Approximately one-third of the reports (nine out of 28) are investigating people with mental health problems from ethnic minorities. In date order of publication these nine are Campbell (1988), Clunis (1994), Harry (1994), Buchanan (1994), Woodley (1995), Grey (1995), NG (1996), Mabota (1996) and Nicholson (1996).

Location of Services and Question of Integration
The earliest of the reports considered concerns the care and treatment of Sharon Campbell and discussed what it describes as 'the black dimension' (Campbell, 1988, para. 16.27). The report is interesting in its approach to recommending policy, saying that a deliberate policy to set up community facilities for minorities would be inadvisable because it 'could hamper, rather than forward, integration' (Campbell, 1988, para. 16.27). It argues that such a policy would lead to disputes about allocation of resources on a fair basis between different community groups. However, the report does recommend that 'the location of community mental health centres should take account of the needs of ethnic communities' (Campbell, 1988, para. 16.28).

Ethnicity Addressed?
Despite the fact that much is known about the over-representation of black people in the criminal justice and mental health systems, as well as the problems of institutional racism, the Buchanan Report, for example, does not address the issue of ethnicity. It is mentioned only in passing: 'Michael Buchanan was born on 31 July

1964 of afro-caribbean origin' (Buchanan, 1994, para. 4.2). However, the Buchanan Inquiry team recognised the importance of involving black mental health organisations in the debate the issues gave rise to, but regrets the fact that the groups approached did not choose to contribute (Buchanan, 1994, para. 2.15). The Grey Report is even less satisfactory. Grey's race and culture are totally ignored, apart from one oblique reference, 'Kenneth Grey was born on the 14 July 1970 to Jamaican immigrant parents' (Grey, 1995, p9). No attempt is made at understanding the impact his ethnicity may have had on such matters as diagnosis, treatment or services offered. It may be that the Grey Inquiry team itself struggled with the suggestion made in the Clunis Inquiry that 'the added factor of his blackness may have contributed to the diffident manner in which some professionals treated him, and it may have caused them to defer against his best interests, to his own expressed wishes' (Clunis, 1994, para. 3.1.5).

However, the Woodley Report published by the same health authority and at the same time as the Grey Report has addressed this issue at considerable length and is consequently much more useful. The sensitivity of services to SL's cultural needs is examined in some detail and constructively debated. For example, it looks at the reasons for over-representation and what this actually means:

> The lack of access to, and appropriateness of, preventative and support services to black/ethnic minorities, compounded by socio-economic disadvantage, leads to overrepresentation of black/ethnic minorities in the psychiatric hospitals system. (Woodley, 1995, p153.)

But despite the Woodley team's wide-ranging and detailed analysis of the issues for mental health professionals and service users in respect of making services more user-friendly to black/ethnic minority user groups, other reports do not appear to see the need for such an approach. A notable example is the NG Report in which the issue of ethnicity is overtly disregarded. 'We mention one matter which is capable of being significant but which we are able to put to one side' (NG, 1996, p24). NG is a Kenyan Asian whose victim, a stranger, was also Asian. The London borough in which NG lived according to the 1991 census had an ethnic minority population of 24.4%. While the report acknowledges that 'mental health services are failing to meet the needs of ethnic minority communities nationally' it dismisses the issue of race and ethnicity in NG's case in two paragraphs by concluding, 'We did not find any evidence or suggestion of racial prejudice or discrimination in the provision of services to NG' (NG, 1996, p24). The report does not appear to have considered the ethnic origins of NG's clinical team members or whether they had any understanding of the effects of racism and discrimination. The report's complacency on this matter is indicated by its superficiality. An examination by the inquiry team of the local mental health services and community care strategy is considered sufficient to absolve them of the need for further investigation of any underlying problems such as institutional racism.

Evidence of Racism
The Clunis Inquiry team was also mindful of the need to consider the possibility of racism and 'tried throughout [their] investigations, to keep a close eye on any evidence of prejudiced attitudes towards Christopher Clunis', but concluded that they did not find 'any prejudice or discrimination in relation to [him], save a willingness to accept too readily that he had abused drugs' and also that 'young black males should not be type cast as suffering from schizophrenia unless the clinical indications warrant it' (Clunis, 1994, p4 and p129). The over-representation of black people diagnosed as suffering from schizophrenia concerns the Clunis Inquiry team, which states that 'it has been confirmed that the proportion of black people amongst those detained under the Mental Health Act 1983 is high in relation to other ethnic groups' (Clunis, 1994, p129). The Campbell Inquiry also comments on what it describes as a tendency for there to be an 'over-diagnosis of schizophrenia in the black minority population' and the difficulties this poses for doctors. The report concludes that training of all mental health professionals must address the issue of recognising and responding to the needs of people from different cultural and ethnic backgrounds (Campbell, 1988, paras.16.29-16.30).

The Harry Inquiry investigating the deaths of Jason and Natalia Harry, whose mother, Sharon D, a British-born African-Caribbean, struggled with the dilemma of diagnosis and cannabis use. (At the time of the offence Sharon was subject to Section 37 of the Mental Health Act 1983.)

> It is not easy, even now, to be sure of the diagnosis of Sharon's psychiatric condition. Psychotic breakdowns due to marijuana are usually brief and the greater length of her second episode suggests a schizophrenic illness (Harry, 1994, para. 11.7).

The issue of cannabis use by black people leads the Harry Inquiry to recommend multiethnic consideration of the issues relating to cannabis use and how to protect those vulnerable to its effects (Harry, 1994, para. 12.18). This report explores the importance of understanding the problems of African-Caribbean service users and comments how it is 'vital not only to give specific attention to ethnic factors in conferences, supervision etc. but always to record the process' (Harry, 1994, para. 12.10). Here African-Caribbean social workers included the chair of child care conferences and two social workers.

The Woodley Report offers much more insight into the complexity of the issues for black mental health service users than any of the other reports studied. SL's mother had suffered from an untreated mental illness throughout SL's childhood and in tracing his family's experiences of services, the Woodley Report concludes:

> Awareness of racial and cultural differences, and the effects of discrimination, either in terms of their life experiences, or members of the family's treatment by social services, appears from the records never to have been addressed (Woodley, 1995, p17).

Similarly, the private psychiatric hospital in which SL was detained for a period is criticised in the report for its lack of sensitivity to the needs of its black patients, the social worker being the only staff member who was considered to have appreciated 'the race dimension to his care'. This is despite the high proportion of inpatients from black/ethnic minorities – 44% according to the director of nursing (Woodley, 1995, pp39-40). In contrast the drop-in facility developed in SL's home area (Newham) by the social services department was seen as being much more appropriate (Woodley, 1995, p69). However, SL's father resigned himself to an expectation that services for black people would be of poor quality. 'As a black boy, I know my son will be drugged up in your prison and hospital. I don't expect the best for my son, I expect the worst.' (Woodley, 1995, p120.)

The Woodley Inquiry also draws attention to the failure of mental health services to respond appropriately to the needs of ethnic minority communities, citing institutional racism as the major cause of this fault (Woodley, 1995, p133). The report seeks to influence the health service agenda in addressing this issue by detailing the problems currently experienced by black and ethnic minority communities in gaining access to mental health services appropriate to their needs. For example, there are less likely to be alternatives to hospital admission offered to all minority groups. There is greater use of police powers under mental health legislation and greater use of compulsory powers of detention as well as increased use of locked wards and secure facilities. To ensure effective services for black and minority ethnic groups, various strategies are suggested which include implementing equal opportunity policies, monitoring and recording the use made of services by black and minority ethnic groups in addition to identifying and resolving the problem of racism.

> Racial harassment remains a serious problem and includes not only physical attacks, but verbal abuse and more covert or surreptitious gestures such as exclusion. If this is not dealt with effectively and fairly, an environment conducive to recovery and good health can never be achieved for black and minority ethnic people. (Woodley, 1995, p137.)

Without a strong emphasis on black user involvement local services cannot be effectively evaluated and developed to bring about change. A more detailed look at the processes and consequences of institutional racism and over-representation can be found in Woodley (pp154-6, for example).

Furthermore, the Woodley team addresses the very real problems for black service users and staff following the fatal incident in Newham and the need for senior staff to manage the situation assertively. They state:

A key area which we feel received insufficient attention, on which action should be taken, is issues raised for black service users and also black staff by the incident and its aftermath. We heard that the fact that SL is black and BB [the victim] was white resurrected some historic tensions in the service in the form of racist remarks. This is against a backdrop of two Inquiry Reports published in 1994 concerning black/Caribbean men with severe mental health needs in the Inner City who killed members of the public. . . Senior managers and supervisors should now take a lead to address such concerns with staff and service users – to this end we trust that the findings of this Independent Review will be of assistance (Woodley, 1995, pp125-6).

Need for Interpreters
Two reports (Mabota and Nicholson) highlight the importance of providing adequate interpreter facilities. In the case of Kumbi Mabota, who originated from Zaïre, English is his fifth language (Mabota, 1996, p6). On assessment, the psychiatrist stated 'it was difficult to get a history from him because of the language difficulty' Mabota, 1996, p12), although the ASW involved in the assessment indicates 'Mr Mabota's need for a French speaking interpreter' (Mabota, 1996, p16). Although it might be self-evident that understanding a person's mental health problems requires good communication, this is spelt out by the Woodley Report reiterating that skilled understanding of the 'nuances of behaviour and language are of special importance, given the nature of mental health problems' (Woodley, 1995, p136).

Communication is so fundamental to understanding a person's mental health needs that language is central to the discussion in the Mabota Report. This results in the report recommending basic requirements for interpreters such as competence in the relevant foreign language and a good command of the English language as well as skills in the context of mental health (Mabota, 1996, p62). The inquiry into the non-fatal stabbing of a GP by Maria Caseiro, who is Portuguese, says that she herself drew to the attention of the inquiry panel that there was an 'absence of any inter-preters during her hospital stays despite her requests' (Nicholson, 1996, para. 11). In the words of the Woodley Report, 'a profound shortage of bilingual professionals and skilled and trained interpreters with an understanding of racial, cultural and mental health issues further compounds the problem [of understanding service provision]' (Woodley, 1995, p135).

Section 117 Aftercare and the Care Programme Approach
Background to Policy Framework
The quality of aftercare is central to any community-based mental health inquiry. The whole process of hospital admission, treatment, and discharge, with an effective aftercare package underpins community care for the mentally ill. Providing services which enable some of the most vulnerable people in society to engage in a therapeutic alliance to ensure good mental health while minimising risk to the individual and others is the key to successful mental health care. In 1991 the Care Programme Approach (CPA) was introduced in England to formalise this framework for providing services to the mentally ill in the community (Department of Health, 1990, HC(90)23/LASSL(90)/11). Inquiries before this date, such as that of Campbell, make recommendations which are in essence advocating such a policy (Campbell, 1988, recs 22-27).

The core elements of the CPA consist of a detailed needs assessment, a comprehensive and agreed care plan, a named keyworker, and regular review of the patient's progress. Users and carers must be involved in care plans as far as possible (Department of Health, 1995, para. 1.3). Building Bridges also claims that the CPA 'is the cornerstone of the Government's mental health policy' (para. 3.0.3). Several inquiries outline the working of the CPA. For example, 'Learning Lessons' states that 'the purpose of the Care Programme Approach is to ensure the support of mentally ill people in the community in order to minimise the possibility of losing contact with services and to maximise the effect of therapeutic intervention' (Nicholson, 1996, para. 65).

Health authorities have responsibility for the CPA while social services departments have responsibility for care management under the NHS and Community Care Act 1990, but the principles underlying both processes are the same. The CPA applies whether or not a patient has been detained under the Mental Health Act 1983. Health and local authorities, in co-operation with voluntary agencies, also have a statutory duty under Section 117 of the Act to provide aftercare services for people who have been detained under Section 3, 37, 47 or 48 of the Act. Again the principles underlying S117 and the CPA are the same.

From April 1994, all health authorities in England were required by the Department of Health to maintain supervision registers for those most at risk (Department of

Health, 1994, HSG(94)5). Section 25 of the 1983 Mental Health Act came into force in April 1996 to provide supervised discharge for people detained under certain sections of the Act if additional supervision is thought to be indicated (Mental Health (Patients in the Community) Act 1995). It should be noted that CPA and supervision registers are requirements in England but not Wales. The mental health legislation applies to England and Wales but differs in Northern Ireland and Scotland, although supervised discharge does operate in Scotland.

Government guidance on the discharge of mentally ill people to the community states:

> In a number of cases where something has subsequently gone wrong, poor coordination of services or communication between those involved has been a major factor. . . The Care Programme Approach requires close inter-agency and inter-personal working (NHS Executive, 1994, (HSG(94)27/ LASSL(94)4, para. 14).

The Mursell Inquiry which investigated the care received by Martin Mursell who killed his stepfather and seriously injured his mother, draws out very clearly the dangers of fragmented and poorly managed aftercare services.

> Care in the community for severely mentally ill people is the right policy, but it comes with a number of risks . . . these risks can be greatly reduced if, before the discharge of a patient into the community, proper assessment is made of the degree of risk posed to the patient and to others, and a plan drawn up detailing the arrangements for aftercare and setting out the goals to be achieved. (Mursell, 1997, para 10.2)

In response to difficulties experienced in providing comprehensive aftercare, more-recent inquiry reports examine the quality of the aftercare provided and the adequacy of the risk assessment upon which decisions are made. To this end, inquiries now include in their terms of reference an investigation of aftercare usually by questioning how well the CPA was working. An example of this can be seen in the NG report which relates to a patient who had recently been discharged from hospital and was subject to the Care Programme Approach. The terms of reference for the inquiry include examining

> the extent to which NG's care corresponded to statutory obligations, partic- ularly the Mental Health Act 1983 (including the Care Programme Approach, Supervision registers, and the discharge guidance; and local operational policies (NG, 1996, para. 1.2(ii)).

Similarly, the Taylor Inquiry's terms of reference are derived from the need to investigate the quality of aftercare provided to both Keith Taylor and his father William Taylor. The terms of reference therefore seek to find out *inter alia* about

1. the quality and scope of health social care and risk assessments;

    the appropriateness of their treatment, care and supervision;

    the extent to which local policies were adhered to in care plans;

    the extent to which care plans were: effectively drawn up, effectively delivered and complied with by Keith and William Taylor.

2. the adequacy of collaboration and communication between the agencies involved and the agencies and the Taylor family (Taylor, 1996, ppix-x)

CPA Criteria

One of the obvious features of these reports is that although in some cases the individual concerned was clearly subject to statutory aftercare because of his or her previous detention under the Mental Health Act 1983, in many cases the patient in the community had no such history with the result that the need for formalised aftercare with a care plan was more uncertain. Local interpretation of the criteria of the CPA varies and hence the safety net that should be in place does not always seem to be as effective as policy intended. For example, Armstrong, Boland, Burton, Hampshire, Smith, and Viner did not meet the criteria for any formalised care planning.

Additionally the different levels at which the CPA operates can mean that some people may be assessed as needing less care than others so that a minimal CPA does not involve the whole team. If the patient needs a medium level of support a more complex CPA is indicated and the third tier is aimed at ' individuals with severe mental illness, suffering from severe social dysfunction, whose needs are likely to be highly volatile, or who represent a significant risk, are likely to require a full, multidisciplinary CPA' (Department of Health, 1995, para. 3.2.5). The Viner Report recommends screening to eliminate the dangers of not offering aftercare to all those who need it (Viner, 1996, recs 20 and 27). This inquiry also draws attention in its report to the need to include an assessment of the carer's needs in the CPA assessment 'especially when that person is elderly and the burden is unshared' (Viner, 1996, p70, see also recs. 16-18).

In the case of Smith, local CPA policies and procedures were in place. The hospital allocated Smith to level one based on its assessment which did not include a social work assessment of his home and family circumstances. Level one 'meant that there was no special planning of care for [him] subsequent to his discharge' (Smith, 1996, p.17). As the report says later, 'the designation of "Care Programme Approach" status is crucial to the level of aftercare' (Smith, 1996, p48). Because of insufficient assessment by the hospital team inadequate information was conveyed to those following him up in the community. Smith returned home to live with his family. Shortly afterwards he killed his mother and half-brother.

Other reports outline the CPA criteria that applied locally in more detail. For example, the Armstrong Report explains how the local hospital had 'implemented its own basic CPA in 1991' and that in 1993 changes in the criteria for inclusion had been made. Previously the criteria had only applied to patients admitted to the psychiatric ward and therefore excluded those admissions to the acute ward following episodes of serious self-harm. Also the earlier criteria had not mentioned the importance of risk assessment. (Armstrong, 1996, pp29-30.) Nevertheless, Armstrong was not considered to fall within the CPA criteria. He was diagnosed as suffering from a personality disorder with social and addiction problems and was not assessed as suffering from an enduring and treatable mental illness. The hospital team also decided that he was not vulnerable in the community despite his risk of self-harm and that therefore the CPA did not apply. The inquiry took a different view arguing that Armstrong was eligible for the CPA,

> in view of the history of his admissions and the apparent reason for them,
> namely breakdowns in relationships, homelessness, self harming,
> attempted suicide and admitted alcohol and drug dependency
> (Armstrong, 1996, p43).

One of the issues highlighted by this inquiry is that none of the agencies involved ever had all the relevant information to enable a complete assessment to be made.

In the hospital Trust that treated the Taylor family the criteria for the CPA applied if the patient had:

- been detained under the Mental Health Act (except sections 3 and 37);

- stayed in hospital for 3 months or more;

- three or more admissions in the last year;

- two or more episodes of serious deliberate self-harm (DSH) in the last year;

- an enduring mental illness with an emphasis on those with a history of poor compliance. (Taylor, 1996, para. 1.6.)

Before Keith Taylor killed his father in 1995, he had been admitted to hospital three times within a year and therefore met the CPA criteria. William Taylor probably also met the criteria because of his enduring mental illness (he suffered from dementia), although this is less clear. The report addresses these issues explicitly. In William Taylor's case there was a failure to implement the CPA. This was considered partly responsible for the fact that neither care team knew the extent of the other's problems. The team caring for William Taylor failed to become aware of Keith Taylor's second and third admissions to hospital. Keith Taylor's second admission to hospital took place less than a month after his first and arose because of suicidal feelings. The inquiry team argues that this should have triggered an assessment of his ability to manage when discharged but there was no planned aftercare. There was no system for referral to the ward's social worker, who was on annual leave at the time of Keith Taylor's discharge. The inquiry concludes that Keith Taylor's hospital treatment was too medically dominated with insufficient attention paid to his social circumstances or family stress. 'The responsibility of the hospital does not cease at the point of discharge and continues while the patient is an out-patient.' (Taylor, 1996, para. 7.8.)

Problems of Implementation
In some reports, such as Newby, Stoker, Sinclair, Viner, and Boland, the implementation of formal aftercare procedures was slow to take effect despite the official implementation date of 1 April 1991, and one of the outcomes of holding inquiries has been to speed up the process. The Stoker Inquiry maintains that the CPA was not a relevant factor because the local policy was not due to be implemented until 1 April 1995 (Stoker, 1996, p39). In Oxfordshire the CPA was not implemented until October 1994, although the Newby Report states that, in Rous's situation, 'even if the Care Programme Approach had been introduced in Oxfordshire by 1 April 1991, it seems unlikely that John Rous would have been subject to CPA', for two reasons. He had not had a recent hospital admission and he was not subject to any section of the Mental Health Act 1983 (Newby, 1995, p59).

In Taylor's case 'a major issue for the inquiry team was whether [the CPA] had been implemented and if not why not'. The Trust and social services protocol required the CPA to be implemented by 31 August 1994 (Taylor, 1996, p1). The Taylor Inquiry is unusual because the carer was mentally ill and the identified patient, his father, suffered from dementia. This inquiry identified two basic areas of concern:

> First, was the question of the formal implementation of the CPA. Second was the question whether, quite irrespective of the implementation of the CPA, the patients . . . had received reasonable levels of support and care after discharge. There is an inherent risk in emphasising formal processes

at the expense of individual care. All staff at all levels have a responsibility to observe good practice and concern for their patients which cannot be achieved only by rigidly following procedures. (Taylor, 1996, para. 11.)

The Taylor Inquiry concludes that although the tragedy may not have been averted if the CPA had been fully implemented the chances of avoiding it would have improved.

The CPA is not an alternative to best practice and common sense. It should be seen as an enhancement of best practice and common sense and may act as a check and a framework within which the adoption of best practice and common sense can be ensured. (Taylor, 1996, p62.)

The NG Report acknowledges that CPA procedures were being modified and improved following the tragedy but of the report's 17 recommendations 10 relate to the implementation of the CPA. The inquiry entitled 'Learning Lessons' states firmly, 'it is clear that the Care Programme Approach was not implemented satisfactorily during [the patient's] hospital stays' (Nicholson, 1996, para. 70), and eight of the 28 inquiries' recommendations reflect this concern to improve the working of the CPA. The Viner Report makes the point that 'this case highlights the inadequacy of the limited implementation of the CPA which was adopted in Dorset' (Viner, 1996, p89).

One of the few inquiries that is complimentary about early CPA implementation is the DU Report. It is also unusual in that DU's CPA keyworker, a community psychiatric nurse, was a designated care manager. It is one of the few inquiries that considered the discharge and aftercare arrangements to have been well planned and effective.

However, one of the report's conclusions is that although the systems of care management and CPA were well developed, the relationship with services was complex leading to an organisational weakness arising out of a lack of clarity of purpose (DU, 1993, para. 5.13). To rectify these weaknesses the report contains a number of recommendations relating to the CPA (DU, 1993, recs 1-4).

Another report that also congratulates local services on the thoroughness of their CPA and Section 117 aftercare arrangements is the Mitchell Inquiry. The documentation, however, was said to pay less attention to difficulties in Mitchell's interpersonal life and concentrated on recording the care and treatment programme (Blom-Cooper, 1996, p162). Although the report makes recommendations about systems to review placement breakdown, its comments are generally favourable:

The Care Planning, Section 117 system and Care Assessment system were all complied with, were all appropriately multidisciplinary in approach and form the basis of a sound process. (Blom-Cooper, 1996, 164, see also recs. 11 and 39.)

Section 117 Aftercare

Although inquiries distinguish between aftercare provided under the mental health legislation and that provided as a result of DoH guidance in the form of the Care Programme Approach this is a somewhat academic and arbitrary distinction. The Buchanan Inquiry team when looking at S117 procedures highlights the point made earlier by the Taylor Inquiry. Whatever the procedure followed it is no longer a defensible policy to separate the reasons for admission to hospital from what happens afterwards. The Buchanan Report is critical of the hospital's repeated pattern of hasty discharge with insufficient attention to ensuring that adequate aftercare arrangements were in place. Buchanan had 13 hospital admissions over a period of approximately 10 years interspersed with numerous custodial interventions in response to his offending behaviour. On his last admission before committing his index offence Buchanan was admitted under Section 37 of the Mental Health Act 1983, but this admission only lasted 22 days; 18 days later he robbed and seriously assaulted a 70-year-old man and two days later killed a stranger in a car park.

Prior to Buchanan's discharge the Section 117 meeting 'failed to identify a keyworker who would be responsible for his aftercare in the community'. The failure to allocate responsibility to one named person is considered by the inquiry panel to be 'an unacceptable lapse in attention to the patient's care' (Buchanan, 1994, para. 6.20).

Reference to threatening people and stealing had no effect on the decision to discharge as quickly as possible. Knowledge that he was dangerous was of secondary importance to the need to discharge him from the ward (Buchanan, 1994, para. 6.17).

The Buchanan Report makes several important recommendations with respect to the discharge of Section 117 patients or via the Care Programme Approach (Buchanan, 1994, recs 1-7). Where the patient has a history of offending, the Buchanan Report suggests that the discharge planning meetings should be attended by representatives of the police and Probation Service.

The Stoker Inquiry is also concerned with the adequacy of Section 117 aftercare. In Stoker's case he was subject to a restriction order (Section 41 of the Mental Health Act 1983). However, there seems to have been no system in place to ensure formal planning and review.

> There does not appear to have been any formal discharge meeting involving the profession recognised as appropriate by Section 117 of the Act. Community Psychiatric Nursing involvement did not occur until 1993 and there is no record of any Section 117 aftercare meeting. We cannot trace that at any time a formal Risk Assessment process was in place . . .
> (Stoker, 1996, p37).

Nor, it seems, was there 'any formalisation of the Care Programme Approach in his case, and indeed the CPA in Northumberland was not implemented until 1994' (Stoker, 1996, pp37-38).

Supervision Registers
The supervision register is a development of the Care Programme Approach in England and seeks

> to ensure that those patients who posed more risk to themselves and others received special care support and supervision within the community to assist in preventing them from falling through the care network
> (Stoker, 1996, p38).

The three categories indicated for being placed on the supervision register are: significant risk of suicide, significant risk of serious violence to others or significant risk of severe self-neglect (Department of Health, 1994b). As the Robinson report indicates the register is not a statutory register as is the child protection register, but is intended to act as a means of identifying those in most need of resources (Blom-Cooper, 1995, p195). The Stoker report makes the point that because of Stoker's conditional discharge from the Mental Health Review Tribunal in 1987 which ensured that he received statutory aftercare, including him on the Supervision Register 'would have made no difference to the management and care . . . but would have ensured that regular review meetings would have been held every six months' (Stoker, 1996, p38).

Compliance with Aftercare and Other Problems
Compliance and the lack of compulsory powers to ensure that aftercare is accepted by the patient is an issue for many inquiries such as Armstrong, Buchanan, Clunis, Mursell, Sinclair, and Stoker.

The Buchanan Report highlights the dilemmas facing professionals who knew, when discharging Buchanan from hospital, that he had 'a propensity for violence and was likely to be uncooperative with post-discharge arrangements' (Buchanan, 1994, para. 6.27). There is also the problem of when to end or discharge these responsibilities. In the case of SL, the S117 statutory aftercare was discharged three weeks before the fatal incident occurred (Woodley, 1995, pp85-90). According to this report, 'the multidisciplinary assessment under the Care Programme Approach . . . was fragmented in respect of SL and militated against proper review' (Woodley, 1995, p89). The report goes on to say that there was no assessment of his longer term needs and that the decision to discharge him from social services was premature.

Training in CPA and S117
The Clunis Inquiry is concerned that mental health professionals who are responsible for providing aftercare do not necessarily understand that the principles underlying S117 and the CPA are the same (Clunis, 1994, p109). Three years later the Mursell Report still indicates that 'professionals within the mental health service did not clearly understand how to operate the Section 117 MHA aftercare procedure' (Mursell, 1997, para. 10.33). Multidisciplinary and multiagency training is strongly advocated by several inquiries in order to promote inter-agency working and understanding of the mental health legislative framework. For example, reports that emphasise the importance of training include Armstrong, Clunis, DU, Mursell, NG, Nicholson, Sinclair, Taylor, and Woodley. The Armstrong Report makes the point that initially the CPA was seen by staff as something special and not as 'part of a philosophy of treatment [which] should be an integral part of normal psychiatric services' (Armstrong, 1996, p42). Training was seen as necessary, therefore, not just to understand the procedures but more fundamentally as a prerequisite for changing the culture and philosophy of care. Without training, however, operational difficulties are unlikely to be resolved.

Operational Difficulties
What these examples from inquiries reveal is the difficulty practitioners have in making the procedures work and some of the reasons for this. Therefore, managers need to address these issues. How do different professionals in different agencies with differing administrative systems and structural approaches to service provision achieve co-operative joint working? The complexity on both a professional and structural level should not be underestimated. The social services investigation into the tragic outcome of Sinclair's care in the community has this to say:

The failure of ward staff to involve the social worker in discharge planning and care programme approach reviews, or to provide information such as Care Programme copies, discharge summaries, or even to notify Social Services Department of discharge is more accurately described as a non-system than a system failure. (Sinclair, 1996, para. 5.4.1.)

But even when systems are in place, problems frequently remain. The Stoker Inquiry is one that reiterates the need for each member of the care team to take responsibility for multidisciplinary communication and collaboration and to recognise their joint role in managing risk safely in the community (Stoker, 1996, p45). Training will go some way towards improving the situation but unless it is undertaken on an interagency basis and is continually updated it is difficult to see the problems being resolved. The Viner Report strongly recommends joint training, emphasising the importance of including housing staff (Viner, 1996, rec.12). The Sinclair Report spells out the competencies required by keyworkers operating the CPA in their recommendation about training (Sinclair, 1996, rec.10).

What is important for improving practice is to introduce systems which make it possible to measure outcome in order to inform clinical decision-making. This point is emphasised by the Kirkman Inquiry which concludes that unless decisions about discharge and aftercare plans are subject to audit and monitoring the quality of decision making cannot advance. The inquiry team argue for routine monitoring of how well guidance is followed rather than waiting until something goes wrong (Kirkman, 1991, p30, see also rec. 2). Such emphasis on the effectiveness or otherwise of the CPA leads one to speculate as to why it does not exist in any formal sense in Wales. One particularly tragic example of the inadequacies of community-based services comes from the Isle of Man where there is also no CPA. In this instance the Joughin Report states that the CPA approach should be adopted on the Isle of Man (Joughin, 1997, para. 6, 108).

Housing Issues and Inquiry Reports
Many inquiries cite housing issues as being central to the difficulties in providing adequate aftercare to people suffering from severe mental health problems.

Homelessness and Mental Illness
It has long been recognised that the prevalence of mental illness among homeless people is far higher than in the general population. The Newby Report cites some of the evidence for this, quoting figures ranging from a prevalence that is 10 times higher among homeless people than the general population to a figure of 20 to 25 times higher (Newby, 1995 para. 6, 2). For many people, the experience of home-lessness itself is a major precipitating factor leading to poor physical and mental

health. For others their mental health problems lead them into homelessness, and of course these two problems interact. The task for housing and other agencies providing social and medical care, particularly in inner cities, should not be under-estimated. People who are homeless often have multiple problems and by virtue of their homelessness are more likely to have trouble maintaining contact with services. Conventional models of service provision are inherently unsuited to meeting the needs of people with a mental illness who are also homeless. For some their problems of homelessness and mental illness are compounded by problems of substance misuse. What becomes clear from inquiries, such as Newby (1995), is that more-assertive outreach services combining the provision of both housing and care are needed in order to address some of these issues.

Appropriateness of Accommodation

Other inquiries, notably Clunis (1994), Buchanan (1994), Woodley (1995), and Mursell (1997) identify the inadequate range of housing provision available, which then often leads to the use of bed and breakfast accommodation because there are no alternatives. Such reports are consistent in their criticism of the use of such accommodation, arguing convincingly that it is unsuited to the needs of all people suffering from mental health problems of any severity. The Woodley Report, for example, is clear on this matter: 'bed and breakfast hotel accommoda-tion should not be used for people with mental health needs' (Woodley, 1995, p106, see also rec.18).

What is needed is accommodation that offers different levels of support and super-vision – from intensively staffed hostels to independent living with packages of care tailored to the needs of the individual. In the case of Clunis, for example, at times he was accommodated in DSS resettlement units which according to one unit manager operated as 'the last resort for people whom nobody wanted' (Clunis, 1994, para. 20.1.3) but which are ill-equipped to cater for their residents' complex needs, particularly if treatment of severe mental illness is one of them. The Clunis Inquiry argues that such a unit 'was a totally inappropriate place to care for someone . . . with a severe mental illness' (Clunis, 1994, para.19.2.1).

The Rooney Inquiry was one of the earliest to identify the importance of meeting someone's housing needs in order to maintain good mental health and minimise risk (Rooney, 1992). The limited range of accommodation in the community, much of which is provided by the private sector, results in less than adequate discharge arrangements. The Carr Report, 1997 (paras. 8.4.5 and 9.5.13) recom-mends that local government authorities 'should take urgent action to review the provision of appropriate housing for mentally disordered people moving to the community' (Carr, 1997). Carr's wish for his own independent accommodation alongside the lack of available housing caused him to reply to an advert in a shop window for a living-in child-minder. Later, he set fire to this house and the mother and her two children died in the fire. As the focus on psychiatric care shifts from hospital to community so there needs to be greater variety of imaginative care packages which are needs-led and provide flexible levels of support at different times. This view is endorsed by Alyson Leslie in her comprehensive investigation into the case of Susan Joughin who killed one of her two children and attempted to kill the other (Joughin, 1997). She also argues for greater understanding on the part of housing officers of the problems arising for people suffering mental health problems (Joughin, 1997, para. 6.81).

Pressures on the Carer
Several inquiries have now taken place because someone suffering from a severe mental illness has killed a close relative (usually the mother) with whom they were living. (More detail is given in the section on risk assessment and management.) Boland lived with his elderly mother in a two-bedroomed 14th-floor flat and although his need for independent accommodation had been acknowledged, nothing had materialised (Boland, 1995). Similarly, Viner lived in his mother's house and, despite the evidence that this was very stressful for Mrs Viner, the situation continued because her son was extremely resistant to any move to alternative accommodation (Viner, 1996). Sinclair's living space was even more oppressive. He lived with his mother and brother in a small one-bedroomed flat, designed specifically for an elderly single person. This degree of overcrowding meant that he and his brother alternated between sleeping on a sofa and on two armchairs pushed together (Sinclair, 1996). Like Boland and Viner, Sinclair killed his mother. Increased recognition of the burden placed on carers is one of the clear recurring messages to emerge from successive inquiries and has led to an increased awareness of the importance of assessing the needs of carers independently of the relative with mental health problems.

Mursell killed his stepfather and attempted to kill his mother. One of the main contributory factors identified by the ensuing report was that Mursell 'was given very little help to find adequate accommodation, which resulted in him having to live in unsuitable conditions with his mother' (Mursell, 1997, p1). The inquiry team acknowledged that Mursell was difficult to help and challenged the housing authority's systems and services. At one stage accommodation is described as being 'at the heart of the aftercare plan', which in this case was Section 117

Aftercare. However, the keyworker, a social worker, was too inexperienced to operate effectively in this role and had insufficient understanding of housing procedures to ensure that appropriate housing was secured (Mursell, 1997, p56). This leads to recommendations for joint training for housing and social services to develop shared understanding of respective responsibilities. In addition, the report recommends that health, housing and social services must work together at a strategic level to develop and co-ordinate appropriate services for mentally ill people (Mursell, 1997, p104). As a response to these difficulties some local authorities have combined housing and social services departments under one management structure with a view to integrating the separate functions.

Confidentiality and Housing
Another of the clear messages which needs to inform policy making so as to change practice is the apparently common tendency to withhold information about a person's psychiatric and/or offending history from the housing agency on the grounds of confidentiality. Too often the practitioner seems afraid to disclose information for fear of jeopardising someone's chances of being offered suitable accommodation. There are many reports that highlight this phenomenon, such as, Clunis, Buchanan, and Woodley. The Kirkman Inquiry is unequivocal in its rejection of such practice, 'the information which was given to the Housing Association about Kirkman and his fiancée was *'totally inadequate for [the housing association] to make a considered allocation of housing in the interest of neighbours'* (Kirkman, 1991, p32). Yet the earliest of the inquiries studied here, that of Campbell, consider it to be 'understandable' that there was a 'reluctance to communicate confidential information to the management of voluntary hostels or bed and breakfast hotels or, save in support of housing applications, to housing staff' (Campbell, 1988, para. 16.10). Fear of breaching medical confidentiality is mentioned in the Boland Inquiry as an issue which sometimes hinders decision making with regard to allocation of accommodation by the housing department.

However, the overriding message from inquiries can be illustrated by the Woodley Report's emphatic statement that mental health workers when helping service users to apply for housing must disclose information about risk whenever the person has a history of violence (Woodley, 1995, p106). The Carr Report argues in favour of 'disclosure of psychiatric history to a housing authority if there is potential dangerousness' while balancing this against the need to protect the privacy of people suffering from mental health problems (Carr, 1997, para. 17.7.3).

Residential Care and Inquiries
Broadly, the cases studied fall into three categories in relation to the sort of accommodation people are in at the time the offence is committed. Some have absconded

from hospital care and are unaccounted for in the community, notably Grey, Mitchell, and Mabota. Others are living with family members in significant levels of stress, such as Boland, Hampshire, McFadden, Sinclair, Smith, Taylor, and Viner. A third group have been placed in accommodation of their own with varying levels of support, for example, Armstrong, Buchanan, Clunis, Kirkman, Mursell, NG and SL (Woodley). This group tend to have a history of housing problems, including failed hostel placements often because of violent incidents. They are often reluctant to accept the services offered.   One person (Robinson) was in hospital when the offence was committed (Blom-Cooper, 1995).

Residential care does not feature strongly in the inquiries. The only report in this study involving a resident in a residential home is the DU Inquiry. This report finds the overall standard of care is good but that the home had insufficient infor-mation to accurately assess DU's needs (DU, 1993). Residential care for those with mental health problems who are not elderly is limited. This was considered the accommodation of choice for Stoker, when his capacity to look after himself in the community was diminishing.   However, the home, after considering the referral, did not accept his application. With no alternatives to turn to, Stoker was left in deteriorating circumstances in the community until the offence took place. Rous was living in a Cyrenian hostel when he killed Jonathan Newby, who was on duty as a care worker at the time (Newby, 1995).

One report 'Caring for the Carer' examines the circumstances which led Keith Taylor, the carer, to kill his father, William Taylor, who suffered from an acute confusional state. This report draws attention to the immense difficulties facing the son who became the principal carer after the death of his mother. Although the father was assessed as needing residential care, his son had difficulty accepting that he could not provide the care his father required. As the pressure on the son increased he developed severe mental health problems, but was reluctant to acknowledge his own needs, with tragic consequences (Taylor, 1996).

Longer Term Housing Provision
As early as the Campbell Report was published, the limitations of short-term hostel accommodation was recognised (Campbell, 1988, rec 28). This concern is restated by the Carr Inquiry team (Carr, 1997). Here the problem is referred to as insuffi-cient consideration of 'medium-term housing needs'. The Carr Report develops its arguments for taking this view which include 'the importance of stressing contin-ually the reality of housing need' (Carr, 1997, para. 7.3.5). It also gives rise to a recommendation that the relevant NHS trust:

. . . should ensure that high priority is given to the initiation of medium-term housing plans at an early stage in discharge planning in cases where hostel accommodation is anticipated to be relatively short term, and that local housing agencies be involved in the preparation and execution of these plans (Carr, 1997, 7.3.7 and 8.4.4).

Chapter 4
Professional Implications

Lessons for Psychiatry

Introduction

Although all of the 28 inquiry reports reviewed contain important implications for psychiatrists, perhaps the surprising conclusion that can be drawn is the relatively low profile that psychiatry seems to hold within this context. This may be because on the whole psychiatrists were assessed as having acted in the best interests of their patients and to have acquitted themselves fairly well. There were, however, exceptions to this and certainly there is no room for complacency for either the medical profession or other mental health professionals.

The Psychiatrist's Role in the Multidisciplinary Team

The main issues to arise include the role the consultant has within his or her team (Smith, Stoker, Mitchell, Robinson, NG, Woodley), whether he or she is accessible, approachable, how easy or difficult is it for more junior members of the clinical team to voice their concerns and have them heard, and communication issues. The issue of power and how it is used cannot be ignored. The role the consultant adopts within the clinical team is crucial because it directly affects the functioning of the team, how its individual practitioners operate and how the service to the patient is delivered. Obviously it is not just the consultant whose role is important, a thorough and correct understanding of the roles and responsibilities of each member of the team is essential for effective multi-disciplinary working (Blom-Cooper, 1995, p138).

Nevertheless, the consultant has the lead role as Responsible Medical Officer (RMO) and with this goes the ultimate responsibility to ensure that the patient is treated in the least-restrictive conditions possible while at the same time ensuring public safety. In reality of course the RMO has to rely on other team members who have more of the day-to-day management of the patient, for example the consultant responsible for Stoker's care saw herself as taking the lead role 'in all decision making', while relying on those in the field who had more contact with him (Stoker, 1996, p22). Therefore the consultant needs to ensure that working relationships within his or her team are based on respect and trust and avoid team tensions that lead to team dysfunction and the resulting weaknesses in service delivery.

In a more recent report the consultant was criticised for leaving too much of the patient's care to unqualified staff, 'too great a reliance was placed on the nurses and OT Assistants (OTAs) to be the "eyes and ears" of the Doctors, when they had

163

not been adequately trained for the role expected of them, nor had they been adequately informed about [the patient's] forensic and psychiatric history'. Throughout a two-and-a-half-year period, during which time the patient was for the most part in the community, the consultant saw the patient twice and on three further occasions he was seen by three different junior doctors (Smith, 1997, p16). An additional feature of this inquiry is the concern expressed by the panel that the relaxed and cosy nature of the consultant's relationship with the team was in fact detrimental to proper assessment and treatment planning. 'This very informality . . . was responsible for what we believe was the Team losing sight of the key issues and objectives in relation to Paul' (Smith, 1997, p15).

More frequently the problem seems to be that the views of staff are in some way weighted according to their rank and status. Examples of the RMO not taking all members of the team seriously can be seen in several reports, such as Stoker and Mitchell. The inquiry into Mitchell's care says that doctors seemed to 'marginalise or invalidate the contribution of "peripheral" and unqualified staff' (Blom-Cooper, 1996, p62). Despite such criticisms the quality of the psychiatric care given to Jason Mitchell was considered to be of a particularly high standard: 'Patients like Jason Mitchell . . . do not always receive such committed, long-term care from general psychiatry services' (Blom-Cooper, 1996, p242).

Clinical and Managerial Structure
Close to not working co-operatively as part of a team lurk the dangers of working in isolation, highlighted in several reports – for example, Sinclair and Robinson. The latter inquiry talks of the consultant at one stage in Robinson's care as being 'a solo player' with a 'working style which omitted regular multi-disciplinary discussion with others involved in the patient's care' (Blom-Cooper, 1995, p67). The 'lone practitioner', working individually increases the risk of unsound decision-making. As described by Blom-Cooper, 'the individual practitioner is prone to catastrophic errors of judgement' (Blom-Cooper, 1995, p135 and p137).

The structure of the service influences practice and the Sinclair Report, for example, suggests that hospital services and in particular the consultants remained detached from the CMHTs. 'The consultants regarded themselves as already under too much clinical pressure to devote time to membership or leadership of the CMHTs' (Sinclair, 1996, p19). Fragmentation and lack of medical commitment to community working are identified as the cause of considerable difficulties.

The hospital service was separate from the community services; those services were separated within themselves. . . . These structural inadequacies were directly relevant to the failures in Raymond Sinclair's care . . .

Senior doctors have a key part to play in management in the further development of this framework, and as a part of this endeavour should become full members of the CMHTs, in which they should take a leadership role. (Sinclair, 1996, p53-4.)

Inflexibility of care is a further structural characteristic that is not uncommon. For example, the Doherty Report outlines the consequences if the approach to care is not holistic. Doherty did not fit well with the system and certain procedures were inflexible. He was admitted to hospital for a few days on two separate occasions, neither of which included a Thursday. The result was that the patient was not discussed at the weekly ward round which only took place on Thursdays and so was never seen or discussed by the consultant (Doherty, 1995).

Similarly, errors in clinical judgement are considered in some inquiries to be partly a result of poor communication between the consultant and ward staff who had important information, as well as inadequate skills on the part of the junior doctors (for example, Sinclair, p60). The inexperience of junior doctors is considered from the point of view of adequate supervision being available, leading to the recommendation: 'Consultants should ensure that trainee doctors are regularly supervised, and that the job description of both reflect this commitment' (Sinclair, 1996, rec.4). The role of senior registrar is often not well defined, leading to confusion about responsibility and when deputising for the consultant is appropriate. In the case of Sinclair this led to revised job descriptions for senior registrars being recommended (Sinclair, 1996, rec. 5).

Level of Staffing

The excessive workload carried by some consultants was a cause for concern and was seen by some inquiries as contributing to deficiencies in patient care, for example Stoker, Sinclair, Woodley, and Armstrong. The Harry Inquiry describes the consultant psychiatrist as being 'heavily burdened' and recommends 'the freeing up of more time for liaison, community visits and communication with professionals who are unable to attend Ward Rounds' (Harry, 1994, rec.17).

The Armstrong Report suggests that insufficient numbers of psychiatrists led to unacceptably high waiting lists and that the poor staffing situation was exacerbated by a locum consultant who remained a locum for 11 years (Armstrong, 1996). Likewise the Hampshire Report states that there were 'grossly inadequate resources for what is being expected of the Mental Health Team' (with one consultant responsible for a population of 80,000 with a clinical assistant to deal with the outpatient clinic) (Hampshire, 1996, p47). In the Sinclair Report it is reported that whereas the Royal College of Psychiatrists recommendations for staffing are one consultant psychiatrist to a population of 35,000 to 40,000, the consultant responsible for Sinclair was almost single-handedly responsible for 110,000 (Sinclair, 1996, p18). The report also suggests that the excessive workload was responsible for inadequate assessment and that overwork contributed to not achieving sufficient standards in clinical practice (Sinclair, 1996, p38 and p41).

Discharge and Follow-up
The involvement of the psychiatrist in the process of discharge is another major focus of inquiry reports. The quality of the information at discharge, to whom it is sent and how quickly, has been a concern of many inquiry teams. Discharge letters to GPs are often a source of criticism. In the case of Armstrong, for example, the discharge letter to the GP was written by a junior doctor but not checked by the consultant, leading to inaccurate, misleading and unhelpful information being sent to the GP (Armstrong, 1996, p53). Another example of insufficient information being conveyed in the discharge letter can be seen in the Boland Report, the criticism here being that the letters were too medically oriented and narrow. In the case of Sinclair the information given to the GP was 'full, although inaccurate in certain details, contrasting with the paucity of the information sent to the workers who were to implement this care plan. The letter was, however, eight weeks late' (Sinclair, 1996, p33). The report goes on to explain that the information available at discharge was inadequate partly because the family's views were not considered (Sinclair, 1996, p56). The Mursell Report draws attention to the dilemma faced so often by the RMO, of discharging patients because their mental state has been sta-bilised in hospital, while knowing that relapse is all too likely because of a reluctance to comply with the care plan. Mursell, who killed his step-father and attempted to kill his mother, had 'regularly threatened violence to his mother' (Mursell, 1997, p66). Prior to the index offence he had several compulsory hospital admissions so that 'the clinicians all knew about his potential for violence, his drug misuse, his failure to keep out-patient appointments and his non-compli-ance with treatments' (Mursell, 1997, p74).

The Psychiatrist's Role in Aftercare
The quality of the aftercare in place is particularly pertinent to most inquiries, and whether improvements in the service would have averted the tragic outcome is obviously a crucial question to be answered. The part played by psychiatry in Section 117 aftercare and the Care Programme Approach is well understood but needs to be fully endorsed by psychiatrists. In some of the cases examined it seems that the psychiatrist was not always comfortable with the role and the

responsibilities that were inherent in the aftercare package. Aftercare is often difficult, not least because of the reluctance on the part of the patient to acknowledge its importance for his or her mental health. While retreating behind the traditional medical role of prescribing medication is an inadequate response to the challenge of community care, it is understandable that apprehension may get in the way for the consultant or RMO entering the uncertain arena of multiprofessional working. Acknowledging these difficulties may be the starting point along with a preparedness to support one's multidisciplinary colleagues.

Complex social problems often accompany medical ones and the prospect of finding solutions particularly when resources may seem woefully inadequate is often daunting. The medical model when emphasised to the exclusion of social factors and home circumstances was criticised by reports such as Boland, Mitchell, Robinson (in parts), and Taylor. The Smith Inquiry states that the medical view was far too narrow and ignored the assessment of the social and family context. Anthony Smith killed his mother and half-brother approximately one month after being discharged from his first admission to hospital when he had been diagnosed as suffering from paranoid schizophrenia (Smith, 1996).

Added to this, the additional problems of substance abuse make managing risk safely through good aftercare practice and procedures more difficult. This is highlighted in several reports, such as Armstrong, Mursell, and Stoker. In the case of Armstrong the consultant is criticised for not referring Armstrong formally to a drug project, having identified his need for such help (Armstrong, 1996). The Harry Report is concerned at the lack of understanding by psychiatry of the dilemmas of cannabis use and its effect on mental health: '. . . there is a view that cannabis use in the black community is excessively blamed by white Psychiatrists as a cause of psychotic disturbance' (Harry, 1994, para. 11.6).

Other reports which illuminate the correlation between substance abuse and illness and how this increases risk include Grey (1995), Viner (1995), Armstrong (1996), Newby (1995), Sinclair (1996), and Blom-Cooper (1996). A criticism sometimes levelled at the medical profession is a tendency to rely too heavily on a diagnosis of drug-induced illness, for example in the case of Jason Mitchell (Blom-Cooper, 1996, p11).

Psychiatry, Risk and Communication Issues
Managing risk safely in the community must be considered a priority for mental health workers of all professional backgrounds and is considered from a multidisciplinary perspective in the section on risk assessment and management. (see pp131-42)

However cynical it may sound, risk itself can be a force for cohesion within teams. Yet in some reports (Stoker, for example) the consultant did not meet with the team to assess the risk despite requests to do so from other team members. Stoker was living in the community on a restriction order, having previously been detained for the manslaughter of his mother-in-law many years earlier. Despite this history there was no formal risk assessment. The inquiry states: 'The responsibility for . . . failings and shortcomings in the management and care must lie with the Care Team – but primarily with the Supervising Consultant Psychiatrist . . . as being the Team Leader' (Stoker, 1996, p48). Concern about the lack of risk assessment leads the Stoker Report to recommend protocols for risk assessment and risk management (Stoker, 1996, rec. 5).

In the case of Armstrong, the poor history taken on admission with no attempt to verify it led to missed connections and an inability to assess risk adequately (Armstrong, 1996, pp56-57). Armstrong was a serious abuser who had been sexually abused himself, 'the product of incest between his mother and his maternal grandfather'. Given what is known about abuse the report thought it surprising that at 'no stage had the Consultant, or indeed any of those caring for Armstrong, made any effort whatever to discover any further details about the alleged incidents and whether they in fact happened' (Armstrong, 1996, p56).

Other issues affecting risk concern communication. Communication between doctors is an issue which is identified by the Mabota Report. Mabota was found guilty of the death of his girlfriend, Lidie. Language difficulties beset the doctors assessing Mabota (English is his fifth language). Also his admission to hospital was precipitated by a serious act of self-harm in the form of consuming a large quantity of bleach. Mabota was transferred between hospitals without adequate documentation to accompany him, thus making it much more difficult for doctors subsequently treating him to assess the risk accurately. The problems were further compounded by a reluctance on the part of the medical profession to take seriously the concerns about the risk to Mabota's girlfriend expressed by the police. The presenting problem of self-harm was the focus of medical concern. The report considers with the benefit of hindsight that it was

> unfortunate [that the doctor] did not incorporate any reference in his notes to the Police Officers' fears that Mr Mabota might murder Lidie. None of the doctors who subsequently came to treat Mr Mabota or to carry out a risk assessment upon him were, therefore, aware that the Police at any rate perceived Mr Mabota to be a serious risk to Lidie's well-being (Mabota, 1996, pp18-19).

Poor communication between psychiatrists and other team members is seen in many reports as a more frequently occurring problem, for example Sinclair (1996), Robinson (Blom-Cooper, 1995), and Taylor (1996). The Taylor Inquiry is unusual because it investigates a carer who killed. The report looks at the circumstances surrounding the death of William Taylor who suffered from dementia and was being cared for by his son, Keith Taylor, who had mental health problems of his own. Keith Taylor killed his father when the burden of caring for him, following the death of his mother, became intolerable. Both father and son were receiving psychiatric services, but from different teams. One of the report's conclusions was that the communication between the teams was inadequate to enable proper assessment of the problems. Treating each patient in isolation from the other's situation led to an incomplete understanding of the stress. Furthermore, there was no system to ensure that hospital patients needing aftercare were referred to a social worker by the consultant. At the time of Keith Taylor's discharge the social worker attached to the ward was on leave.

> It is entirely inappropriate for a doctor whose patient has had three spells of mental illness in a short period to discharge him in the hope that the Social Services will become aware of the case and be able to assess the patient's needs (Taylor, 1996, p51).

Poor communication is also seen to be a contributory factor in the tragic outcome resulting in the NG Report (1996). This inquiry, which looks into the circumstances surrounding the death of a woman who was run over in a car-park by a person subject to aftercare within the CPA framework, identifies poor aftercare arrangements as being due in part to the consultant's lack of co-operation in the CPA process. Insufficient commitment on the part of consultants to attendance at S117 meetings is unfortunately a recurring theme in other reports, such as Woodley and Clunis. Another inquiry, this time into the deaths of two young children killed by their mother who was subject to Section 37 of the Mental Health Act, is critical of the fact that the consultant's attendance at child protection conferences was poor, 'resulting in delays in decision making and a lack of joint planning particularly between Social Services and the Medical Services' (Harry, 1994, para. 11.0). Communication problems led to errors in clinical judgement according to the Sinclair Report.

> It has to be a matter of great concern that [the consultant and the CPN] as two health professionals, working in the same Trust and caring for the same patient, should not have had immediate access to each other's records, and indeed to each other for informal contact. It is a reflection both of faulty systems and of an ethos which tended to keep professionals apart (Sinclair, 1996, p47).

Similarly, despite the cohesiveness of the team, the inquiry into Paul Smith's treatment was concerned that the OT records were 'kept quite separately from the medical records', leading to a lack of awareness by the doctors of the patient's difficulties which were recorded well in the OT records (Smith, 1997, p16).

Issues of Diagnosis
The problems of diagnosis and particularly dual diagnosis are mentioned in many of the reports. For example, that on Doherty spells out the complications for placement and treatment that can occur when a patient has a dual diagnosis of personality disorder and mild learning difficulties (Doherty, 1995). Similarly, Armstrong's care was made more difficult with a diagnosis of personality disorder being accompanied by drug and alcohol dependency (Armstrong, 1996). The Mitchell Report contains a lengthy discussion about the problems of establishing a diagnosis in his case and debates the validity of the basis on which it was changed (Blom-Cooper, 1996, pp38-39, 73, 85, 87-88, 172). Difficulties in treatment arising from a change in diagnosis are highlighted in reports such as that on Hampshire. Hampshire was initially treated for symptoms of depression. Later it became clear that he was also severely paranoid with depressive ideation but the lack of clarity about diagnosis may also have contributed to the reluctance to detain Mr Hampshire compulsorily under the Mental Health Act 1983.

Legal Issues
Some reports, notably Viner and Hampshire, consider there was a lack of understanding of the criteria for compulsory admission or perhaps just a reluctance to detain someone. On occasion this may lead doctors to argue that the patient does not meet the legal criteria for compulsory detention. The Hampshire Report questions the consultant's threshold for compulsory admission and is critical of doctors for delegating the responsibility for assessing and monitoring to the CPN. The report concludes, 'Monitoring was not enough. Someone should have stepped in and made an effective decision' (Hampshire, 1996, p53). In addition, the report considers that if a doctor believes someone should be in hospital although is not 'sectionable', yet the patient is refusing informal admission, then 'there must be a continuous process of risk assessment'. Not surprisingly, assessment for compulsory admission to hospital by telephone is not considered good practice by this report (Hampshire, 1996, p72).

Issues relating to conditionally discharged patients under Part III of the Mental Health Act 1983 are addressed in four reports: Kirkman (1991), Robinson (Blom-Cooper, 1995), Mitchell (Blom-Cooper, 1996), and Stoker (1996). Although these issues do not relate only to psychiatrists, the role and quality of decision making of Mental Health Review Tribunals are considered in four reports, Grey (1995),

Robinson (Blom-Cooper, 1995), Mitchell (Blom-Cooper, 1996), and Nicholson (1996). Various recommendations in respect of MHRTs are made, not least the suggestion that MHRT members should receive feedback following their decisions to discharge (Blom-Cooper, 1996, rec. 31) as well as being given adequate training (Grey, 1995, rec. 16 and Blom-Cooper, 1996, rec. 30). Blom-Cooper proposes that, in the case of restricted patients, the medical member of the tribunal should be a forensic psychiatrist if possible (Blom-Cooper, 1996, rec. 6). For other recommendations, see Blom-Cooper (1996) recs. 7, 8, 9 and 22, and Nicholson (1996), recs. 8, 9 and 10.

A further problem from a legal perspective concerns the misinterpretation of the Mental Health Act 1983 as in the Grey Report (1995) or simply not being familiar with policies and procedures, as was the case of a locum consultant treating Mabota (Mabota, 1996). In the case of Grey, the report concludes that wrong interpretation of the Act led to a series of errors regarding sections which in turn led to an absence of Section 117 Aftercare and a lack of appropriate concern when Grey absconded following his transfer to an open ward which had only taken place because of a faulty understanding of the Mental Health Act. 'To say there was a lack of understanding of the Mental Health Act 1983 . . . particularly regarding transfer arrangements from prison to hospital – is an understatement (Grey, 1995, p7). This report contains an interesting discussion of the case in relation to the Mental Health Act (Grey, 1995, pp64-65).

Blom-Cooper reminds us of the RMO's duties which cannot be delegated (Blom-Cooper, 1995, p75, 138 and *passim*). For example, the RMO is not permitted to delegate authorisation of leave of absence to nurses. (Blom-Cooper, 1995). In the case of Grey, the senior registrar wrongly thought she had the authority to make decisions, which resided only with the RMO.

Two reports in particular reflect upon the potential value of guardianship in relation to the situations being examined. Viner, who lived with his mother, was reluctant to accept that her increasing frailty together with his difficulties meant that a move to other accommodation was indicated (Viner, 1996). Blom-Cooper argues that in Robinson's case the assertive use of guardianship had maximised the possibility of safe management in the community (Blom-Cooper, 1995).

Other Issues
A range of other points relevant to medical practice emerge from a careful study of inquiry reports which need mentioning. One concerns doctors taking leave without making adequate arrangements for cover in their absence. This is high-lighted in the NG report which states that there should be 'a policy whereby

consultants and junior doctors should so arrange their leave so that no more than one medical member of a team is away at any one time. A consultant who is going on leave should ensure that the key worker for all patients subject to the CPA procedure is aware of the arrangements for cover' (NG, 1996, rec. 15). The NG Report also draws attention to the question of responsibility for notifying the DVLA if a patient persists in driving against medical advice (NG, 1996, rec.16).

The report Learning Lessons is concerned with a problem that arises because of conflicting opinions between consultants, both of whom have some responsibility for the patient because of the patient transferring between facilities. This leads the report to recommend:

> A policy should be agreed on action to be taken where the clinical opinions of the specialist team and the catchment team differ; where there are irreconcilable differences between the consultants, an independent view from a senior consultant should be taken with agreement to abide by the advice and for the *status quo* to remain in the meantime. (Nicholson, 1996, rec.1.)

Several issues relating to ethnicity are commented upon in the reports. These are referred to in the section on race, (pp143-8) but both the Woodley Report and the Harry Inquiry consider the consultants in question had not addressed the issue adequately.

A final but very important point centres on the role of carers in the management of the mentally ill in the community. Several reports highlight the fact that they consider that insufficient notice is taken by the consultant of the carer: Viner (1996), Mursell (1997), Hampshire (1996), Sinclair (1996), Smith (1996), and Robinson (Blom-Cooper, 1995) are some examples. It is suggested that the consultant is so concerned with his or her patient's rights that the needs and views of the carer are often overlooked.

Implications for Community Nursing
Of the 28 inquiries considered, at least 19 are important from a community nursing perspective.

A number of inquiry reports highlight community nursing because either the community mental health nurse (CMHN) was the keyworker or had an otherwise central role in the individual's care and treatment in the community. Some reports are striking simply because of the very limited involvement of community nurses, 'Community Psychiatric Nurses were notable by their absence' (Doherty, 1995, p61). Often in cases where the community nurse involvement was minimal the report makes recommendations to the effect that had there been a more central role for community nurses the outcome may have been different and the overall care would have been improved, for example the Doherty, Boland, and NG Reports. Others, where the CPN had the lead role or most contact, such as the Viner and Hampshire Reports, suggest other courses of action or intervention would have led to better risk management.

Perhaps the message is that best practice is about proper team working, rather than one particular mental health professional being given responsibility for managing patients in the community whose needs are complex and for whom safe management of risk is crucial. Particular inquiries which concentrate on the role of the community nurse and the difficulties she or he faced and which are considered here are: the Viner Report, the Hampshire Report, the Sinclair Inquiry, the Smith Inquiry and the Stoker Inquiry (all published in 1996).

Recurring issues raised in these reports which need addressing by community mental health nurses and their managers fall broadly into four categories. First, the role of the community nurse and how this is seen by GPs and other professionals, notably hospital services, is examined and also the part played by the community nurse as keyworker together with what this means in practice. Within this category the CMHN's role in assessing and managing risk is fundamental. Leading on from this is the quality of liaison and communication with other members of the multidisciplinary team and with other agencies. Thirdly, the level of experience and training of the nurse and the need for clinical supervision are highlighted in several inquiries. Lastly, a group of managerial issues such as leave and transfer arrangements, caseload size and recording are underlined in some reports.

Role as Community Nurse and Keyworker
Leaving aside the issue of whether the community nurse has a role other than if depot medication is part of the treatment package, there is perhaps the more important matter of the responsibility placed on the community nurse particularly when poor compliance increases the level of concern. For example, in the case of Frank Hampshire, he did not wish to engage with his community nurse who visited him at home, and at the same time he refused to keep appointments with his GP and psychiatrist. There were no other professionals involved in his care. As his mental state deteriorated and his insight decreased his resistance to active intervention increased. This placed a huge burden of responsibility on the nurse, who wrote to the doctor, 'I regret I can only monitor the situation as Frank refuses

to enter into any active care plan' (Hampshire, 1996, p35). However, with the benefit of hindsight it is clear that monitoring was not enough. Frank Hampshire later killed his wife, Catherine Hampshire, who was also his carer. The Hampshire Report makes the point that the CPN's 'continued involvement . . . deflected the focus of the clinical team. Her presence gave a sense of security to both the doctors and Catherine Hampshire and may have contributed to the delay in taking more definite action' (Hampshire, p52). In the words of the report the CPN 'had failed in her remit [to persuade the patient to be admitted to hospital] and had no real role to play thereafter . . . other than a monitoring one' (p52).

In one report the respective roles of the CPN and a community mental health worker (CMHW) were never clarified, leading to confusion and wrong expectations on the part of other professionals. 'It is important that the roles of a community psychiatric nurse and a community mental health worker are clearly understood' (Mursell, 1997, p73). Radcliffe highlights the danger of deploying unqualified community nurses as keyworkers and suggests it is policies rather than individuals which should be singled out for criticism in the Mursell Inquiry (Radcliffe, 1997, p23).

Some reports indicate that it is not unusual for the keyworker not to be formally identified. For example, the Buchanan Report states: 'No keyworker was allocated at the S117 meeting. The CPN said he saw his role as primarily covering the keyworker responsibilities' (Buchanan, 1994, p37). In the case of Robert Viner, who killed his 76-year-old mother who was also his carer, the report comments on the lack of clarity as to the identity of the keyworker. The CPN in effect undertook the keyworking role but the report highlights the need for this to be formalised so that there is no confusion (Viner, 1996). As well as having clarity about role and keyworker responsibilities, the CPN also needs to be clear about the purpose of his or her intervention in relation to that of the multidisciplinary team. For example, this is spelt out in the Mursell Inquiry, 'the absence of a care plan contributed to the poor quality of care' (Mursell, 1997, p68).

Issues of Team-work and Interagency Liaison
The Viner Report emphasises the fundamental importance of working as a member of a multidisciplinary team and not in isolation. Although multidisciplinary teams existed theoretically they did not operate in a meaningful way. 'There was, however, little evidence that the teams actually functioned as teams' (Viner, 1996, p72). The Sinclair Inquiry identifies 'two over-riding themes' of 'fragmentation and lack of medical commitment to community working'.

The hospital service was separate from the community services; those services were separated within themselves. Systems to ensure sharing of information between different professionals caring for mentally ill people . . . were largely absent (Sinclair, 1996, p22).

A lack of an effective team approach was seen as leading to an 'unco-ordinated and disparate service' in the Buchanan Report (Buchanan, 1994, p11). According to Blom-Cooper, team-working was an alien concept while Robinson was under the care of a particular psychiatrist so that although both a CPN and social worker were involved 'they were marginalised' (Blom-Cooper, 1995, p135). 'Although the various team members met together on a regular basis, there was little evidence that there was any real sharing of formulation or planning' (p136). The message seems to be that team-work and communication between agencies is essential for services to be delivered effectively, but that often practice falls short of this to a serious extent. In the Falling Shadow Blom-Cooper offers evidence to suggest that:

> The individual practitioner is prone to catastrophic errors of judgement; the collection of professionals who do not communicate effectively are ill-equipped to design comprehensive care packages. . . The well-integrated team can, on the contrary, design, implement and monitor an effective care package, addressing a wide range of needs. (Blom-Cooper, 1995, p137.)

Experience, Training and Supervision

Almost all reports emphasise the importance of training and clinical supervision. For example, Viner draws attention to the importance of differentiating between support from colleagues and formal supervision, emphasising the importance of the latter. 'If supervision is to be effective, it must be a formalised relationship, with a clear and mutually agreed contract' (Viner, 1996, p78). The report goes on to recommend the 'development and implementation of a supervision policy for all mental health professionals'. It adds that 'any such supervision policy must make explicit the mechanisms that will ensure that every current case managed by a professional is automatically reviewed within a specific period' (Viner, 1996, p79). Similarly, the Hampshire Report recommends that all members of the multidisciplinary team should

> have access to proper clinical supervision . . . [and does] not consider the present arrangements (monthly formal meetings between the consultant psychiatrist and the CPN team manager and informal discussions between the treating doctors and the CPNs at weekly ward rounds) to be adequate (Hampshire, 1996, rec. 10).

The Sinclair Report comments that 'it has not been unusual nationally for nurses working in the community to have no regular supervision of their workload' and views this as most unsatisfactory (Sinclair, 1996, p20). This is also evidenced by Blom-Cooper when at a particular point in Andrew Robinson's career the CPN 'was functioning with little or no supervision' (Blom-Cooper, 1995, p98). He considers the effects of this to have been quite hazardous. 'The absence of effective clinical supervision and enrolled status . . . contributed to an underestimation of the risks involved in Andrew's default from medication.' (Blom-Cooper, 1995, p99.) Discharging patients from one's caseload on the grounds that depot medication has been refused is already a difficult and risky decision, but is all the more so if the decision is made without adequate clinical supervision. The importance of clinical supervision is identified in many inquiries, for example, in the case of Anthony Smith (Smith, 1996, rec 51). Not only was an absence of clinical supervision highlighted by the Sinclair Inquiry as a deficiency in the service but also specialist training was seen as lacking (Sinclair, 1996, p49).

Similarly, the Stoker Report identifies the lack of formal training for community working in addition to the fact that the CPN had not 'undertaken any training with regard to risk management or risk assessment situations' as being a source of concern (Stoker, 1996, p34). The importance of multidisciplinary and multiagency training is a recurring feature of reports into mental health tragedies. Understanding each person's role within the team is crucial if care is to be delivered satisfactorily. In the words of the Viner Report's recommendations, 'all health professionals, who are going to have to undertake a key worker role under the CPA, [should be] involved in joint multi-agency training with housing and social services staff' (Viner, 1996, p41).

Managerial Issues
Lastly, although reports identify practice issues which need addressing, many also underline serious managerial problems. For example, the Sinclair Inquiry comments that 'the principal failure in this case was essentially an organisational one, for which management, both general and clinical, must share responsibility' (Sinclair, 1996, p58). The Sinclair Inquiry is critical of management for not ensuring that structural weaknesses were avoided. Planning for discharge and reviewing aftercare were poor. The inquiry team conclude that care planning was inadequate and that 'the process was unstructured, unreviewed, uncommunicative and unsafe' (Sinclair, 1996, p59). More specifically, inquiries highlight problems such as poor handover of care from one community nurse to another as in the case of Clunis. 'It is unfortunate that [the CPN] did not introduce his replacement . . . to Christopher Clunis before he

left . . . There was too little communication between the various people who were all trying to care for Christopher Clunis' (Clunis, 1994, p32).

Other reports illustrate poor procedures that have resulted in an absence of cover when the CPN is on leave. In the case of Frank Hampshire, who killed his wife, the only regular source of support to the couple at home was from the CPN. 'No proactive arrangements were made for a visit to the Hampshires' during her absence, and the GP was not informed. It was during this time that Frank Hampshire killed his wife (Hampshire, 1996, p39). Hence one of the recommendations of the Hampshire Report states, 'no CPN with primary responsibility for a patient should go on leave without making cover arrangements for high priority patients and without notifying the patient's GP' (Hampshire, 1996, rec. 10). By contrast the DU Report (1993), which is unusual because the CPN was also the care manager, commends the CPN for ensuring that cover was arranged while he was on leave. Despite these arrangements the homicide took place during the absence of the usual CPN, who knew most about his patient.

Discharging patients who do not wish to receive a service from CPN caseloads is a recurring issue which has led several reports to recommend that this should not be done without discussion with the nurse manager or RMO (Buchanan, Clunis, for example). The size of CPN caseloads features as a difficulty in some situations where the outcome has been one of tragedy. 'CPN caseloads should be kept under review and CPN record keeping should be subjected to an internal audit process' (NG, 1996, p36). Recording is frequently considered a weak link in the structure of a service. All reports which make recommendations about recording emphasise the importance of not keeping separate records as well as accurate documentation.

Conclusion
The community mental health nurse, previously called the CPN, has a crucial role in the safe management and treatment of mentally disordered people in the community. Inquiries into what has gone wrong in community care 'make recommendations in the hope that by following them, patients will be able to live safely in the community' (Clunis, 1994, p109). It is the collective responsibility of both practitioners and service managers to ensure that as far as possible these recommendations are heeded.

Implications for Hospital-based Nursing
Importance of the Nursing Model
In all cases where the subject of the inquiry has previously been a hospital inpatient, the role of nursing is examined which leads to a series of recommendations. Of the

earlier reports, such as the inquiry which focuses on Carol Barratt who absconded from hospital while on one-to-one observations, the recommendations point to improving the quality of care through a more systematic approach which should include using the nursing process and instituting a model of primary nursing (Barratt, 1991, recs. 2, 3, 4, 5, and 6).

The Named Nurse
In later inquiries particular reference is made to the role of the 'named nurse' and where such a model is used suggests that nursing practice should not deviate from the theoretical underpinning. For example, several reports are critical of the fact that at the point of admission to hospital the patient was allocated to a named nurse who was on leave at the time, thus leaving the patient without effective nursing oversight. The Grey Report is unequivocal on this point: 'the patient should not be allocated to a Named Nurse who is on leave or off sick at the time of admission to hospital or transfer from one ward to another' (Grey, 1995, rec. 6). This theme is developed in a later recommendation, which emphasises the importance of guidelines and procedures to ensure continuity of care when patients are transferred from one ward to another (Grey, 1995, rec. 17).

Mabota absconded from hospital shortly after being transferred from a locked ward to an open one and was subsequently found guilty of killing his girlfriend. The operational policy which provided for a named nurse from the transferring ward to meet with the patient in advance of the transfer was not adhered to. The report suggests that had a named nurse been allocated this might have averted the absconding, or that his absence from the ward might have been detected more quickly (Mabota, 1996, p25). The inquiry concluded from the evidence presented to it that 'the Named Nurse system was a system which existed in name more than in substance' (Mabota, 1996, p57), and that the system was poorly understood. This was considered to be in part because clinical supervision for nurses was inadequate (Mabota, 1996, rec.3 (b)). Also, the importance of clear documentation in the form of a current nursing care plan is underlined by the Mabota Report (Mabota, 1996, rec. 3(a)). Nursing care plans are similarly criticised for being too superficial in the Taylor Inquiry. Moreover the inquiry's findings state that the reason for the inadequate care plan and the delay in formulating such a plan arose as a result of allocating the patient a nurse who was not on duty (Taylor, 1996, pp50 and 62-63 and rec. 7).

The Doherty Inquiry endorses the policy of providing continuity by allocating the patient the same named nurse on recurrent admissions to hospital. However, it considers the practice in the case of Doherty to be applied too rigidly, on the grounds that it is unwise to allocate the same named nurse as allocated on a previous admission, if he or she is on leave. Also the expectation that continuity of care would follow from the named nurse knowing the patient from a previous admission did not happen in practice, nor did it lead to comprehensive care plans or adequate documentation. 'The Inquiry Team were concerned that the named nurse appeared to be more of a theory than actual practice on the ward' (Doherty, 1995, p37).

Role of the Named Nurse
The role of the 'named nurse' is examined in detail by the Smith Inquiry team, giving yet another example of fragmentation of the 'named nurse' system. This was Anthony Smith's first admission as a psychiatric inpatient and although a care plan was drawn up on his first day in hospital no named nurse was nominated at the outset, and the stated policy of allocating 'associate nurses' was not operating in the case of Smith. Furthermore it was not standard practice for the 'named nurse' to attend clinical meetings where the patient's care and progress were regularly reviewed by the consultant, leading to decisions about discharge being made without involving the named nurse. 'The "named nurse's" absence from multidisciplinary meetings is most surprising and wrong. As is the failure to nominate a "stand-in" to cover absences' (Smith, 1996, p49). Several of the inquiry's recommendations focus on the need to improve nursing practice in the light of this experience (Smith, 1996, recs. 3-8, 43-48, and 51).

The Armstrong Inquiry investigates the involvement of nursing in Armstrong's care in some detail. In the course of five voluntary admissions to three different wards in a 15 month period many nurses had been involved in Armstrong's care. The report expresses concern about some of the nurses' interpretations of policies and procedures as well as some of the practices themselves. Again although the named nurse system was adopted in preference to team nursing, one such named nurse allocated to Armstrong on his last admission, according to the notes had no knowledge of this. The report's recommendations in respect of nursing include improving communication by clarifying the role and responsibilities of nursing staff, and also emphasis is placed on the importance of nurses taking a full history on admission (Armstrong, 1996, recs. 2, 3, and 6).

Other Issues
Other reports which refer to nursing tend to select rather different issues concerning them. For example, that on Buchanan makes little comment about the quality of the nursing care received by him other than to say that it appeared that the ward-based staff did not consider fully his risk in the community, but 'were keen

to discharge Michael Buchanan at the earliest possible stage in order to relieve stress on the ward' (Buchanan, 1994, para. 6.11).

On a final point, the Burton Inquiry draws out of its analysis a useful lesson which in this case arises from work done by a student nurse but is equally relevant to all junior and inexperienced staff. Several years before Burton committed his index offence, he had disclosed to a student nurse violent fantasies of harming his parents. This report was never brought to the attention of the medical staff. Although the inquiry concludes that the fact that it was not shared with the clinical team probably made no difference to the outcome, it is important for nurses, however junior, not to feel disempowered in the face of medical staff and to be proactive in making sure significant information is not disregarded.

Social Work and Inquiries

Introduction

Historically, it would probably be fair to say that on occasion there has been tension between the model of mental illness as practised by hospitals and the social constructs that other professionals see as fundamental to understanding ways of minimising dysfunction and maximising mental health. This division has probably been exacerbated by the Mental Health Act 1983, which essentially is a hospital-focused piece of legislation, but which now has to provide the legal framework for people to be cared for in the community. It is perhaps not surprising therefore that the alliance between medicine and social work has at times been an uneasy one. This of course is a simplistic analysis of a much more complex history of differing professional perspectives. However, the reality is that both the part played by medicine and the contribution of social work and other professions to enabling the mentally ill to live successfully in the community are both important and valid. In the words of the Smith Report, 'the failure to recognise fully the social aspects of AS's problems, proved to be one of the most important and unfortunate aspects of his care' (Smith, 1996, p19). What the inquiries do show is that too narrow a medical view of mental illness offers an inadequate framework for assessing and managing risk, while an over-reliance on social factors without sufficient attention to medical treatment and medication is potentially as unsafe. There is also ongoing debate about the merits of different contributions to the care and treatment of those suffering from personality disorder and how best to provide services to meet the complex needs of this difficult group of people, for example in the Carr Inquiry (1997).

Against this background what can social work learn from inquiries? Some answers to this question can be found in Chapter 3 on specific issues which looks in more detail at risk assessment, race and ethnicity, aftercare, and housing.

But in a surprising number of inquiries, such as Boland, Burton, Smith, Viner, and Hampshire, social work is conspicuously absent. The resulting lack of understanding of family and social circumstances leads inevitably to faulty management and treatment strategies. The Smith Inquiry pays particular attention to the absence of a social work assessment and also makes the point that had Smith been compulsorily detained and made application to a Mental Health Review Tribunal, a report on his home circumstances would have automatically followed. The Smith Inquiry concludes that all patients with a major mental illness should have their social situation assessed before being discharged from hospital (Smith, 1996, p41). Another example is evidenced in the Boland Report: 'it is possible, perhaps probable, that reference to Social Services at various points in Alan Boland's treatment might have made a significant difference to the outcome' (Boland, 1995, p27). As a result of social services policy requiring social work to target its limited resources on the seriously mentally ill, a referral for social work may never be made if the initial assessment is too narrow in its focus.

Further difficulties arise because of structural and organisational difficulties. Certain inquiries claim that particular structural models make it impossible to deliver a good service. This can be seen in the Mursell Report, which argues that generic social work is not able to provide effective mental health services. Some inquiries, such as Rooney, Taylor, Boland, Armstrong, and Sinclair, are concerned that the reorganisation of social work services, so that they are no longer hospital based, leads to problems of making referrals and obtaining access to social services provision. The Boland Report reinforces this point (Boland, 1995, rec. 12). In some reports such as Viner and Hampshire the treatment is largely medically orientated with community support being provided by the CPN. As already mentioned, in the case of DU there is no direct social work involvement because the care manager role is undertaken by the CPN.

The lack of experience of some practitioners is another concern expressed in some inquiries, for example Clunis, Campbell, Woodley, and Mursell. Other issues concern such factors as ensuring adequate holiday cover has been arranged. In the case of social work this issue is identified in the NG Inquiry but the problem applies across disciplines and therefore is a recurring theme in other inquiries. Perhaps what is important is the recommendation that there should always be a recognised deputy keyworker who can take over at times of annual or sick leave.

Role of Social Work
A dilemma for social work emerging from inquiries which have a high social work profile is the complexity of role that social workers are expected to perform

and the confusion that this can lead to, especially in the expectations of others. Blom-Cooper highlights this when he says:

> We found that social workers may occupy a number of roles: Named Assessor, Care Manager, Social Supervisor, Appropriate Adult and Approved Social Worker. In the relationship with a service user a social worker may experience not just a lack of harmony, but frequently conflict, because the roles fulfil competing functions. (Blom- Cooper, 1996, p166.)

The balance between care and control is often an uneasy one for social work. The role of Social Supervisor, which requires social workers to exercise considerable responsibility and authority, may not sit comfortably alongside an advocacy role or indeed care management. It is not surprising that for the mental health service user confusion and mistrust of social work can follow. This is probably more likely when the social worker has to take on the duties of Approved Social Worker by making an application for compulsory admission under the MHA 1983. Some reports emphasise the importance of Approved Social Work either suggesting or, as in the case of the Mursell Inquiry, insisting that social workers working with people who suffer from a severe mental illness are Approved Social Workers. 'This is not only sensible, the law requires social workers working with the mentally ill to have a degree of competence' (Mursell, 1997, para. 3.1). This view is also reflected in the Mitchell Inquiry with respect to social supervision of patients on restriction orders (Blom-Cooper, 1996, rec. 24). In the Sinclair Report it is noted that prior to the tragedy social services management reminded staff of their roles and responsibilities, saying they should be 'clearly spelt out', especially when social services is the lead agency. However, what management failed to ensure was that staffing was adequately maintained to meet the needs of people with mental health problems which effectively meant that social workers were unable to fulfil their responsibilities (Sinclair, 1996, p51).

The role of Appropriate Adult is addressed by several inquiries. The Boland Report specifies that this role should be carried out by a social worker with written guidelines produced by the social services department (Boland, 1995, rec. 18, p31). The Mitchell Inquiry goes further by suggesting that the role of Appropriate Adult should be revised and enlarged upon (Blom-Cooper, 1996, rec. 18).

A further social work function highlighted by some reports is that of providing a social history. The distinction between a social and medical history is clearly delineated in the Armstrong Inquiry which advises against leaving this task to junior doctors. 'The social history is to provide information about the social context of the patient and factors which might possibly affect subsequent treatment or care of the patient' (Armstrong, 1996, p37 and rec. 4).

Many of the requests for social work assistance occur because of housing need, for example, Campbell, Rooney, Sinclair, Mursell, Armstrong, and Doherty, suggesting that a major component of the social worker's function is to arrange accommodation. This is accounted for by the nature of a social worker's skills. These include understanding the complexity of community-based systems, such as housing, and being able to negotiate a way through them in order to secure appropriate services. One of the criticisms of the Mursell Inquiry is that the social worker whose task it was to arrange suitable housing for Mursell was too inexperienced with the result that he did not understand how the system for allocating housing worked (Mursell, 1997).

In several inquiries social work came into the frame at a time when discharge from hospital was on the agenda and the person was homeless. Housing alone, however, is often an inadequate response. In the case of Armstrong the inquiry was disquieted to find that although Armstrong was in contact with social workers on 'three separate occasions within a period of fourteen months following threats of self harm on one occasion and overdoses of drugs on the two most recent occasions, the social workers continued to deal with the referrals simply as housing problems' (Armstrong, 1996, p39). Armstrong always presented with an accommodation problem and was never allocated to a mental health team. Although discharge from hospital usually leads to social work involvement if there is at the same time a housing problem, it is not always possible to trace similar links between discharge and social services aftercare. While in Buchanan's case, although social work support was offered after discharge, the inquiry was of the opinion that it was ineffective and was critical of the lack of a team approach. 'The social worker and CPN acted largely in isolation. There is little evidence of effective planning of aftercare' (Buchanan, 1994, para. 44.0.3 (ix)). The frequency of liaison was considered inadequate but it should be pointed out that the level regarded as satisfactory (daily) was probably difficult for any practitioner to achieve. The Rooney Report states clearly that social services should as far as possible 'play a key part in monitoring, those with a diagnosed mental illness who are in the community' (Rooney, 1992, para. 33). The report goes on to say that social services should be notified of all discharges from hospital of psychiatric patients.

The role of social work in aftercare is explored from several perspectives, one being the importance of the social worker if also acting as keyworker to notify not only the multidisciplinary team if there is a breakdown in the aftercare plan but also the social work team manager (Mursell, 1997, para. 3.18 and rec. 6). The section in the previous chapter on Section 117 aftercare and the CPA explores this issue more fully. The common problem of relapse in the community because medication is not maintained leads some reports such as Rooney to debate the issues in respect of community treatment orders and the difficulties facing community mental health workers without such powers. Despite the recent legislation introducing supervised discharge orders (Mental Health [Patients in the Community] Act 1995), this continues to be a contentious controversy which remains unresolved

Confidentiality

An additional source of concern was that while receiving hospital treatment Armstrong was not referred to social services for investigation of the child protection issues, and that because of the perceived need to safeguard confidentiality no one seemed able to address this problem. Yet in November 1992, for example, Armstrong was admitted to hospital following an overdose and on the same day a child protection investigation was initiated, but neither the police nor social services alerted Armstrong's consultant to this. 'The reason given for this failure to transmit information was a possible breach of confidentiality' (Armstrong, 1996 p47). The inquiry team found this 'extraordinary' and debate what difference such sharing of information might have made to the tragic outcome. They see this failure to override confidentiality as 'a breakdown in communication at a potentially crucial stage' (Armstrong, 1996, p48). This example highlights the importance of sharing all available information with those professionals involved if an accurate risk assessment or treatment strategy is to be achieved. The inquiry team accepted,

> the need for confidentiality and the protection of individual rights to some extent, [but] felt that, in many instances, the lives or safety of others was more important than a possible breach of confidentiality and that there should be a better system for the retrieval of information about alleged offenders (Armstrong, 1996, p44).

The issue of confidentiality has implications for all mental health professionals but it is particularly important for social workers to acknowledge the very real difficulties it poses and be proactive in their response. The problems relating to confidentiality and highlighted by successive reports are discussed in the section on risk assessment, in particular with relation to the Smith Inquiry. Smith's wish to withhold consent so that his social and family situation was not assessed by social services had disastrous consequences (Smith, 1996).

Safe Practice in the Community
The report most directly concerned with social work and safe working practices for social work professionals is the Campbell Inquiry which examines the circumstances in which a social worker, Isabel Schwarz, was killed by an ex-patient. Until nine months before her death, Isabel Schwarz had been Sharon Campbell's social worker and had in fact ceased working with her because of Campbell's violence towards her (Campbell, 1988, p5). The issues of experience and supervision, the disadvantages as well as advantages of working in a multidisciplinary team, violence to social workers and the measures that should be taken to manage such risk, are all examined in detail (Campbell, 1988, recs. 3-5, 7-21). Obviously issues of safety for workers occur elsewhere in reports and are not specific to social work, but out of 28 inquiries the only one considering the death of a professional worker is that of Campbell. In the case of Sinclair the community nurse had been threatened with violence on a previous occasion by Sinclair but the victim of the fatal incident was his mother. In the Newby Report, Jonathan Newby, the victim, was an unqualified residential care worker.

Care should also be taken to be alert to the dangers that may arise when a client is dissatisfied with the service provided. The person's mental state may be adversely affected with the result that the person most involved in offering help may become the focus of the patient's hostility and anger. Alternatively the mental health worker may become a part of someone's delusional belief system. What emerges clearly from the Campbell Inquiry is that there was insufficient awareness of the risk of violence that Sharon Campbell posed to others. There was no comprehensive risk assessment or strategy to manage the risk.

The events preceding this tragedy led the inquiry to draw attention to the importance of supervision with recommendations that local authorities should have written guidelines indicating such matters as the objectives of supervision, its frequency, and the necessity for regular, formalised recording of decisions and reviews of patient care (Campbell, 1988, recs. 5, 9,14). The importance of supervision is also mentioned in several other inquiries often linked to the inexperience of some workers, for example in the Mursell report. (Mursell, 1997).

Recording
The issue of recording information in sufficient detail is identified as a weakness in some inquiries, notably Sinclair and Campbell. The trend in social services recording which has emphasised brief recording of fact rather than opinion has had the effect of social work records becoming condensed to eliminate any

possible criticisms of subjectivity. Such minimalist records can militate against comprehensive risk assessment. In the cases of Clunis and Robinson, for example, professionals tried hard to avoid labelling their patients as violent, with disastrous consequences. The Boland Report is more concerned that social services referrals are properly documented and that there is a system for information retrieval (Boland, 1995, rec.19, p31). Similarly, the Armstrong Inquiry discusses the difficulties of maintaining integrated record systems that allow for cross-referencing of information, in this case between child protection and mental health as well as between agencies (Armstrong, 1996, p52).

Implications for Probation Practice
What in particular are the relevant messages from inquiry reports for probation officers? Since the Clunis Inquiry was published in 1994 there have been many others which specifically address the issues of providing services for the mentally disordered offender in the community, and which have direct implications for the Probation Service. Many if not most such homicides are committed by people who have no previous offending history, but a significant minority of recent reports indicate previous involvement with the criminal justice system. Ten of the inquiries in this latter category are considered here. Many of these reports make recommendations that have general relevance for mental health workers from a range of professions while others relate specifically to probation, notably the Stoker Inquiry (Stoker, 1996).

Lessons from the Stoker Inquiry
For example, in the case of Richard Stoker, he was found guilty of manslaughter 20 years before committing a second homicide. He had been detained under the Mental Health Act 1983 until he was conditionally discharged by a Mental Health Review Tribunal in 1987. Following his conditional discharge he was supervised in the community by a psychiatrist and a probation officer until, in 1995, he tragically killed a service user. The inquiry concluded that there was insufficient attention to public safety and too much emphasis on individual liberty, thus seriously compromising the safe management of risk, 'too much consideration was being paid to [Stoker's] own views and preferences rather than what was the prime consideration in the circumstances, namely the safeguarding of the Community' (Stoker, 1996, p48). Given the central role played by probation in this case, a closer look at the findings and recommendations is indicated. The inquiry team's view is that there were clear signs that 'things began to go wrong' indicated by several 'warning signals' (Stoker, 1996, pp16 and 46). Stoker's support network disintegrated, his attendance at outpatients became erratic, his

alcohol abuse increased, there was an increase in his self-harming behaviour, his self-care deteriorated, debts increased and his electricity was disconnected because of unpaid fuel bills. The Probation Service communicated their concerns to the Home Office and contacted the supervising psychiatrist. But according to the inquiry report there was no formal review at this critical time. The lack of appropriate communication and collaboration was the major concern expressed by the Stoker Inquiry, exacerbated by the weak leadership.

As has been found to be the case in many other inquiries, those directly involved in Stoker's care failed to be proactive and there was no adequate multidisciplinary evaluation of the risks that each profession had individually assessed. The major criticism in this case was that 'although there was a recognition and desire to see something done, opportunities were not taken, and the situation was being allowed to drift' (Stoker, 1996, p20). The report emphasises that although the Probation Service was concerned at the inadequate response from the psychiatrist, it failed to do enough and suggests that it could have taken a more direct approach by communicating formally with the Chief Executive of the Mental Health Trust. It is perhaps easier to say this with the benefit of hindsight, but could be important for anyone in this situation in the future.

In relation to risk assessment, the report highlights the fact that the focus of potential risks was of self-harm and the circumstances of the original offence were not given sufficient attention. No connections were made between the pattern of Stoker's situation in 1976 and his personal situation from 1992 onwards. Multidisciplinary reviews did take place but only in response to crises leading to an absence of formal risk assessment.

Common Themes
Many of the issues highlighted are similar to those which relate to other professionals from other agencies. Although the Grey Report stated in 1995 that it was 'not aware of any other reports where the prison and probation services are crucial to the care of the patient', it goes on to say, 'this case was not only an echo of former inquiries but also had far reaching implications relevant to all of the multidisciplinary parties who are responsible for the care, treatment and management of people suffering from mental illness' (Grey, 1995, p6). The main themes to emerge which have general application, focus on communication, confidentiality, risk assessment, and effective interagency and multidisciplinary working.

In the case of Grey, communication and information were generally of poor quality between prison, hospital and probation (Grey, 1995, pp45-46). Confusion arose because of inadequate understanding of the interface between the mental health and criminal justice legislation. Thus the situation arose whereby an offender patient had absconded from hospital with no aftercare plan. The Probation Service should have been involved in the aftercare package because it remained responsible for Kenneth Grey after his release from prison. The report goes on to say that 'this was the point at which the effort to contact [Grey] . . . should have increased, not stopped. There was apparently no local mechanism for solving the problem of maintaining contact with the reluctant patient who needs treatment but does not acknowledge that need' (Grey, 1995, p46). Kenneth Grey murdered his mother 30 days after going absent without leave from hospital. Further evidence of non-existent communication can be seen in the Boland Inquiry. 'No attempt was made to contact or liaise with the Probation Service when Mr Boland attended outpatients while on probation' (Boland, 1995, p13).

In contrast to this the Doherty Inquiry reporting around the same time comments on the quality of the communication between hospital and probation. In this case Brian Doherty, who was subject to a probation order and was admitted to a psychiatric hospital informally, discharged himself from hospital against medical advice (Doherty, 1995, p34). Michael Buchanan's poor follow-up led the Buchanan Inquiry to recommend that 'the Probation Service and Police should be involved in multi-disciplinary meetings prior to the discharge of patients likely to resort to criminal activities' (Buchanan, 1994, p2). Indeed the Buchanan Inquiry team suggested that for mentally ill offenders the statutory involvement of the Probation Service should not be dependent on the length of sentence (one year or more) but should be at the discretion of the courts.

Minimising risk is obviously of paramount importance, and again the Probation Service is seen as having a key role in achieving this, particularly in acting as a bridge between prison and mental health services. The Mitchell Inquiry emphasises this when it says 'probation officers are crucially placed to act as a link between the prison medical service and community health and social services'. Confidentiality recurs as an issue and has implications for probation. The Mitchell Report argues for disclosure of a prisoner's medical records (IMR) to the probation officer where any evidence of potential risk to harm self or others is identified. He suggests that compromise has to be reached to ensure safeguarding the public (Blom-Cooper, 1996, pp263-265). The Doherty Report highlighted the importance of providing the most appropriate care package for at-risk patients when it is not clear which agency should take the lead role, and how in these circumstances probation should be represented on a multidisciplinary panel. Blom-Cooper makes a similar point, also suggesting an interagency approach to case management, and asserts that the Probation Service involved with the case of Jason Mitchell recommends such an approach for mentally disordered offenders .

One of the most critical reports considered is the Armstrong Inquiry. Armstrong had almost a 20-year-long history of probation contact. The inquiry team was concerned at what it considered to be probation's inadequate recording of the reasons for Armstrong's involvement with psychiatric and child guidance services, thus not alerting them later to allegations of inappropriate sexual behaviour. Further criticism was made of the Probation Service because they had not communicated their concerns to social services about the risk to Armstrong's daughters (Armstrong, 1996, pp85-87).

Implications of Ethnicity
Of the 10 inquiry reports considered which have particular relevance to probation four of them are concerned with offenders who are black (Clunis, Buchanan, Grey, and Woodley Reports). The issues raised by these reports are addressed in more detail in the section in Chapter 3 on race, ethnicity, and cultural sensitivity.

Implications for Training
Several inquiries recommend more training: 'there is a need to reinforce and improve the training of probation officers working with dangerous offenders' (Blom-Cooper, 1996, p239). In order to gain better understanding of the roles and responsibilities of other professionals involved joint training initiatives are advocated, for example in 'Building Bridges' (Department of Health, 1995, p38). The importance of training in the understanding of mental illness should not be underestimated. Training in mental health issues was also recommended by many other reports, such as that on Stoker. 'It would have been useful for the Probation Officer . . . to have received more specific training in an area of work which, although having strong similarities with the supervision of life sentence prisoners, also had some significant differences in relation to the mental health background' (Stoker, 1996, p33). This message is reinforced by others such as Kemshall who claims that training in risk assessment and management for probation officers should become more sophisticated (Kemshall, 1996, p141).

Conclusion
The Probation Service has a real role in the assessment, treatment and safe management of the mentally disordered offender, not least because of its skills in addressing offending behaviour. While some offending may be directly related to mental illness (such as that arising out of paranoid delusional belief systems) other offending, for example in the case of John Rous, may be exacerbated by substance abuse (Newby, 1995, p104). Such patterns of offending may require a much more concerted approach which addresses both the addictive and offending behaviour. As the Grey Report states, the Probation Service recognised that Grey

could not address his offending behaviour without first dealing with his drug problem (Grey, 1995, p9). Without a co-ordinated aftercare package, it seems unlikely that psychiatric treatment could be effective. This is also the clear message given in the Buchanan Report. 'The Panel was struck by the candid and helpful input from the probation officers interviewed' (Buchanan, 1994, p21). This sums up the overall conclusion from mental health inquiries which is that the Probation Service has a valuable contribution to make to the care of the mentally disordered offender.

Lessons for General Practice

'GPs have their own agenda, and the care of the seriously mentally ill is not at the top of it.' (Sinclair Report, 1996, p22). This comment, from an inquiry into the care of a mentally ill man who murdered his mother, reminds us that GPs are likely to be involved in cases of serious mental illness. What are the lessons from the inquiries for good practice and organisation in general practice?

This section draws on comments on GP services from 18 inquiry reports which deal with GP services out of 28 published between 1988 and 1997 to present a picture of the problems faced by GP services in very difficult mental health cases and the recommendations that have been made to resolve some of these difficulties. In general, GP services come out of the reports well, being complimented in the Burton and Newby Inquiries for example (Burton, 1996 and Newby, 1995). Although the McFadden Inquiry is critical of the GP involved, it emphasises the commitment and skill of the practice nurse (McFadden, 1995). The Newby Report, for example, compliments the GP on sticking by the patient over many years, keeping colleagues well informed and being aware of important professional issues in the care of his patient.

Communication with GPs

The most common comment is about the psychiatric services keeping GPs informed of the progress, medication, and other treatment of patients referred for specialist psychiatric treatment. Failure to involve GPs is a common pattern and applies also to other professionals. It led to recommendations such as that in the Campbell Inquiry: '. . . that the Royal College of Psychiatrists be invited to publish a document on good practice for discharge and after-care procedures . . . after seeking a consensus with bodies representing nurses, social work, general practitioners, psychology and occupational therapy' (Campbell, 1988, rec. 24). The Rooney Inquiry revealed that although Mr Rooney was admitted to hospital for failing to comply with medication, the discharge letter to the GP failed to mention the medication, the fact that he had been given a supply on discharge or how much it was, and whether the GP was responsible for further prescriptions and ongoing care. When the patient missed an outpatient appointment, the GP was not notified. The recommendations propose amending such uninformative communications which place the GP in the position of not knowing where responsibility lies (Rooney, 1992, recs. 1 and 3). Failure to communicate this kind of information is particularly unfortunate where patients already have a known history of failure to comply with medication. In the case of Boland the GP was sent regular letters, but these were largely descriptive about Mr Boland's fluctuating level of alcohol consumption. The advice given was narrow and unhelpful, being concerned purely with medication, indicating which antidepressant and the dosage to prescribe (Boland, 1995, para. 33). The Armstrong Inquiry recommends clear discharge letters, reporting diagnosis, treatment, follow-up, prognosis, and an explanation of the condition (Armstrong, 1996, rec. 8). The Rooney Report also appends helpful guidance on the layout, timing and content of discharge letters and particular information about behaviour which may show that the public risk of some patients is increasing (Rooney, 1992, App. 2).

The GP as part of the Multidisciplinary Team

Related to this, some of the reports wish to promote a more multidisciplinary approach, including community health and social services staff in initiatives which are often led from the hospital. Thus, the NG Report (1996, p42) recommends inviting relevant agencies '. . . particularly including GPs . . .' to CPA meetings (NG, 1996, rec. 4). Other reports, such as Stoker, extend this by emphasising the key role that should be played by the GP in the safe management of risk of the mentally ill person in the community and the importance of communication between primary care and secondary or tertiary services (Stoker, 1996, rec. 4). The earliest of the inquiries considered here recommends what in effect is a prototype for the later introduction of the CPA, that is, that there should be a multidisciplinary review for patients at an outpatient clinic, day hospital or community centre for patient care involving among others '. . . the general practitioner (or an effective link to him) . . .' (Campbell, 1988, rec. 27).

The Boland Inquiry recommends that the keyworker should be responsible for informing GPs of discharge, with detailed medical letters from the consultant later (Boland, 1995, rec. 8). The Nicholson Report is clear that 'both the key worker and the RMO have a responsibility to ensure that the GP, once known, is briefed at an early stage, with a prompt discharge summary on the case from the RMO' (Nicholson, 1996, rec. 15). Several reports, such as Viner, reiterate that the keyworker role should include ensuring that the GP receives copies of the aftercare plans (Viner, 1996, para. 3.31 and rec. 3). The Viner Report also suggests regular reviews between GP and mental health team, in this case the community psychiatric nurse, even where no particular issues have arisen (Viner, 1996, para. 3.32 and rec. 4). For many mentally ill people, the multidisciplinary team will include parents or other carers, and the Viner Report recommends drawing them into discussions and considering the pressures on them and their home situation which may come to GPs at a time and place unconnected with treatment of the patient (Viner, 1996, para. 3.31 and para. 5.1).

Role of the GP in Community Care
However, GPs involved do not escape all censure. In the DU Inquiry there was the same failure to notify GPs of discharge and change of residence, and the GP role in the care plan was not well defined. None the less, a locum GP is criticised for failing to base prescriptions of psychotropic medication on full information about the history and for prescribing without seeing the patient after a telephone conversation with the residential care home proprietor (DU, 1993, p12). In the case of Frank Hampshire the inquiry found a long-standing good relationship between the GP and the patient's family, but felt that it was almost social. This blunted the GP's objectivity and meant that he did not act firmly and quickly enough (Hampshire, 1996, pp47 and 58). The Sinclair Inquiry found that GP fundholding had contributed to the collapse of a community mental health team, in favour of community psychiatric nurse attachments to practices. GP fundholders also concentrated their funds on many patients with mild disorders rather than the few with more severe problems (Sinclair, 1996).

Weaknesses in information from psychiatric services do not wholly absolve GPs from responsibility in the eyes of the inquiries. The DU Report comments on the importance of GPs themselves ensuring that they are clear about their role in a complex multidisciplinary case (DU, 1993, p14). If the information they receive is unclear, they need to take steps to assure themselves that everything is happening as it should and that they are aware of expectations of them. Equally, if they are taking part in the care of their patient, they have a responsibility to inform the whole team (including, perhaps, consultants, designated keyworkers, community psychiatric nurses, and a nursing or residential care home, if any are involved) of substantial actions that they take. The Armstrong Inquiry found that not enough progress was being made in getting GPs to accept that they should work with all members of the team, not just the consultant. A geographical system whereby GPs' freedom to refer to the consultant of their choice had apparently curtailed co-operation from the GP (Armstrong, 1996, p30). The GP's referral letter in the case of Sinclair contained only sketchy social information and did not alert the hospital team to the full background (Sinclair, 1996, p23). A report that focuses on the events leading up to a homicide over a very short period shows the crucial role of the GP in facilitating communication, as well as the importance of the GP understanding the legal framework for obtaining mental health assessments under the Mental Health Act 1983 (Kopernik-Steckel, 1997).

The attendance of GPs at Section 117 meetings, as well as the difficulties involving them in CPA meetings remain a cause for concern. The Clunis Inquiry, in emphasising the importance of GPs playing 'a full and active part' in multidisciplinary care, advises that they '. . . should be invited to attend S117 Mental Health Act 1983 aftercare conferences *and should endeavour to do so*' (Clunis, 1994, p127 [emphasis added]). This draws attention to the duty on the part of the GP to participate as well as that of the wider team to involve them. GPs must also retain control of their practice team. In the Woodley Report the practice nurse was found to have carried out an initial interview with a transferring patient on behalf of the practice, but no check was made in view of his psychiatric history (Woodley, 1995, p79). For the DU Inquiry team, management of the deputising service was an issue (DU, 1993, p15). In the case of Anthony Smith (1996) the GP was clearly effective in most of her treatment. However, the patient was referred to a counsellor and this was treated as, in effect, a prescription for 'therapy'. The report comments that this should not lead to confidentiality about progress within such activities obstructing the GP's other work and other referrals for specialist help (Smith, 1996, p9). Communication here, according to the report, was effective for the routine, but arrangements between the professionals in the primary and mental health care teams made it difficult to identify and act on more-complex or more-urgent situations (Smith, 1996, p55).

Risk to GPs
Another area where inquiries express concern relates to GPs dealing with patients who present a safety risk to themselves and their practice colleagues and the way they remove them from their lists. Such patients are often difficult and, in the Clunis Inquiry, it was revealed that the GP had removed the patient from his list after a violent incident at the surgery. The inquiry team comments: 'Where the patient may well be psychiatrically ill and in need of prompt care and treatment, this means that less care is likely to be provided when more is in fact needed. (Clunis, 1994, p79.) Later the report states:

> It should not be possible to remove a patient who is mentally ill from the general practitioner's list, without taking steps to ensure that proper care is provided for the patient. We are impressed with the point of view that rejection by a general practitioner suggests that the patient's care and treatment in the community have failed. (Clunis, 1994, p128.)

Several recommendations are made by the Clunis Inquiry in response to their concerns about the role played by the GP, including limitations on the right to remove a patient believed or suspected to be suffering from mental illness from his/her list without giving notice and ensuring suitable alternative arrangements are in place. In addition, further restrictions are recommended preventing removal before another GP is appointed where the patient is on the supervision register (Clunis, 1994, recs. 70-75).

The McFadden Inquiry team (1995, p26) criticise the GP for refusing on safety grounds to visit the patient when protection could have been arranged and for failing to inform himself about the patient's needs. This particular case raises some serious issues for GPs in relation to the risk of violent behaviour posed by a very few patients and where their own responsibilities lie. Another inquiry which raises specific issues for GPs is the report entitled 'Learning Lessons'. The patient attended a GP surgery and stabbed one of the GPs who had come to the assistance of a colleague. Fortunately, the stabbing incident did not have fatal consequences but was nevertheless serious. The report which investigated the circumstances is useful in highlighting some of the subtleties of achieving good practice and making recommendations to improve some of the prevailing weaknesses it identifies (Nicholson, 1996, recs. 11-20).

Chapter 5
Conclusion

This book offers the reader a way of making use of the large number of recommendations emanating from a series of mental health inquiries into community care tragedies which have occurred during the 1990s. Twenty-eight inquiries are considered in detail with their recommendations reproduced in full and indexed to give easy reference. Another six inquiries are also described and referred to in the course of the text. By collating the findings and bringing the information together in this way, readers can draw out the important themes that are relevant for their own situations, depending on where they are coming from – professional practice, policy making, training, or service planning. How mental health services are managed and developed is vitally important. It follows, therefore, that it is crucial that management decisions are properly informed by the wealth of material that is already available. Whatever our own particular roles in understanding and delivering quality mental health services, we all share responsibility for enabling people with serious mental health problems who are living in the community to do so in safety and to realise their own potential.

By listing all the recommendations together in chronological order it is possible to see the range and scope of the information they present, based on individual case histories, available to those currently working in the field of mental health. It is also vital that this knowledge is passed on to students and to those who wish to work in these services in the future. One of the major problems is that many of the recommendations are not implemented. This may be because of insufficient resources, but it is not simply a matter of resources. Unless policy makers are aware of the recommendations, and the training implications for staff are acted upon, similar weaknesses and deficits in service provision will be replicated and the changes needed will not take place. We cannot and should not ignore this extensive and unique resource with which to inform and improve services for people with serious mental illness. As Howlett, on behalf of the Zito Trust, states, 'each of these inquiries (on individuals and on key areas in this field) contains implications which, if implemented, would certainly improve the provision of care and lessen the risk of failure' (Howlett, 1997, p175).

When first hearing (usually through the media) about a homicide committed in the community by someone with mental health problems, it sometimes feels as if the policy of community care is floundering against the weight of the demands it is being expected to meet. But by gaining a greater grasp of the issues and learning what can be done to achieve better services, it becomes possible to feel empowered as a professional mental health worker to improve services, rather than to feel defeated by the range of difficulties often associated with this area of our welfare system.

Undoubtedly, there are still very real problems which require further work before they can be resolved, for example the difficulties surrounding the issue for some people, of compliance with medication while in the community. But the fundamental message is clear: inquiries are not saying that the policy of community care is wrong in itself, or that people should remain in hospital needlessly, but are telling us that we must use them to inform how changes to current practices should be made so that we can learn to develop and improve the way the policy is delivered and managed. The purpose underlying this book is to convey the message that we can all learn from experiences elsewhere, that we can improve the quality of our risk assessment and better the structures and practices in the sphere of interagency and interprofessional communication.

Although initially the proliferation of inquiries into community care tragedies conveys a disturbing picture with negative implications, suggesting that mental health professionals are somehow getting things wrong, the conclusion I draw from this study is that by using this material constructively we can provide better services for the mentally ill in the community. The important messages to be learnt are that we need to be proactive and clear about our role and responsibilities. Good communication with colleagues and other agencies is vital. Working co-operatively as a member of a multidisciplinary team is essential to both assessing and managing risk safely. Using training and supervision effectively is the key to ensuring confidence in our skill and capacity to offer imaginative services that are grounded in sound practice. Likewise, policy makers and managers need to understand the complexities of the needs of those with a severe mental illness and the mentally disordered offender so that the structures are in place for optimum service delivery.

Inquiries, if used properly, go some way to extend our knowledge and thereby enhance our practice. Given the difficulty of assimilating the findings of such a large number of inquiries published in quick succession, I have collated the recommendations to assist planners, policy makers, practitioners, and trainers. To make the best use of inquiries, we need to continue to find mechanisms that allow the findings and recommendations to inform decision making, training, and service delivery.

What do inquiries achieve?
However, there is a view widely held that the high number of inquiries which have already taken place now decreases the likely value of future inquiries, and that the money spent on them could be better used to improve services. What do inquiries achieve? There are many outcomes at a local level, both positive and negative. Locally there seems to be more chance that recommendations will be implemented. For example, in Dorset following the deaths of Robert Viner and his mother, who was also his carer, policies have been put in place to ensure that carers receive an independent assessment of their own needs (Viner, 1996). It is self-evident that an inquiry will have greatest impact at the time of publication and in the locality in which the tragedy occurred.

At a national level the lessons from inquiries tend to get 'lost'. Inquiry overload is a problem which this book tries to address by bringing together a broad range of inquiries with a complete set of easily referenced recommendations. It is necessary to harness the knowledge gained from the extensive range of inquiries heretofore for future reference, and this book represents one way of trying to achieve this. The Zito Trust, set up following one of the most publicised failures of community care (Clunis, 1994), campaigns as a pressure group to achieve improved services for those with a mental illness who are most vulnerable and has done much to raise public and political awareness. However, this is not something that can be achieved by one organisation or government department or mental health agency alone. Structural changes, greater resources, particularly in the inner cities, and a whole range of other approaches in the form of improving levels of knowledge, skills, and competence of the workers involved is required to provide better services for those suffering from severe mental illness. This book sets out to contribute to that process, focusing on practice, with a constructive outlook tempered by realism.

What does the victim's family gain from an inquiry?
Although an independent inquiry is often considered to be helpful for the victim's family there are, nevertheless, many lessons to be learnt about what is helpful and why. There are examples of the family feeling let down by the inquiry findings, thus compounding feelings of loss and anger, for example the families of Rosie Palmer (Armstrong, 1996), Anthony Smith (Smith, 1996) and Martin Mursell (Mursell, 1997). We need to look very carefully at how best to help the families of homicide victims. Increasingly, in the present political and social climate, the rights of victims to have access to help and information are being recognised. So far, work in this area has developed for victims of serious crime when the offender does not have a history of mental illness, but one way forward for mental health

197

services is to be far more proactive in the way information is given to the families of victims of mentally ill offenders. Independent inquiries may satisfy to some extent the victim's family's need to know what happened, but often they do not achieve this and leave the family with much unresolved grief and many unanswered questions.

Also there are far more victims than there are inquiries. What about the victims of attempted murder or violent rape for example, whose attacker receives a mental health disposal instead of a prison sentence? The needs of these victims must also be recognised. My view, after this study of inquiries, is that victims and their families should be entitled to information in much the same way as victims of offenders who are not mentally ill. I would advocate that mental health services need to learn from the Probation Service and I hope that the promised consultation paper from the Home Office and the Department of Health will lead to guidance to make this possible (Rock, 1996). The process of contacting victims is controversial, primarily because of the issue of medical confidentiality and for this reason may require primary legislation before it can happen. But practice guidance which makes provision for all victims of serious offences, committed by mentally disordered offenders, to be contacted to receive and give information could make a real contribution and may achieve far more than the present inquiry process.

If victims' families are contacted by mental health professionals and given the opportunity to have their views, wishes, and needs taken into account, the process of risk assessment would be enhanced by the quality of the information available as a result. Measures such as these could go some way to restoring public confidence in community care which, if judged by recent media coverage, is low. Howlett (1997) maintains that inquiries offer families their only opportunity to find out what happened and why. While for a relatively few victims of mentally disordered offenders the significance this may have for them should not be disregarded, it ignores the needs of many others. Inquiries are not the only way to provide victims' families with some kind of answer, and a lot more could be done outside the inquiry process if political and professional motivation allowed. Johnston (1997), when examining the importance of contacting victims from a criminal justice perspective, argues persuasively for the value of communication and information sharing with victims and their relatives to reduce their anguish and distress.

Do we still need inquiries?
Given the problems of inquiries already highlighted, it is time for a radical reappraisal of this current piecemeal approach to the need to investigate problems in

caring for severely mentally ill people in the community. If the mandatory requirement to hold inquiries following a homicide is retained, it has been argued, for example by Eastman (1996), that the administrative machinery and the publication of inquiry reports should be systematised. However, it may be more constructive at this stage to revise the guidance so that decisions about when to hold inquiries are more selective. Eastman maintains that 'the established body of knowledge that is currently available from inquiries determines that future inquiries should be set up only on the basis of "screening in" those homicides where it is suspected that new learning could be achieved' (Eastman, 1996, p162). This may of course be a contradiction in terms: without the inquiry how can new learning be suspected?

So although there is much to learn from the findings of existing reports, there is little to be said in favour of continuing with such a costly and unsatisfactory process for formulating social policy and improving mental health services. The information that is already available needs to be more accessible. This could be undertaken by a central body such as the Department of Health so that the available information is properly disseminated. The advantage of the DoH taking on a stronger role would be that it could also produce guidance to inform service development in the light of the collation of significant findings. Alternatively, the Mental Health Act Commission could, through the vehicle of their biennial reports, extend their remit to include updated summaries of the important recommendations (Mental Health Act Commission). Also the Mental Health Act 1983 Code of Practice which already sets out to promote good practice could do so with the findings of inquiry reports in mind (Department of Health, 1993).

Alternatives to inquiries

While it remains essential that professional practice and public concerns are effectively monitored and managed, it is questionable whether the present system of inquiry reports allows this to be possible. An alternative approach would be to develop a comprehensive audit of the standards of services, with careful monitoring and systems which could be activated to correct deficits that have led to unsafe practices. The commissioners of services might be best placed to undertake such a task and would be in a strong position to achieve the required change in services which they are purchasing. If the current political agenda removes the power of the internal market then a more appropriate way forward may be to adopt some of the strategies already in place for improving other services. For example, the model which exists within the education system, with a variety of ways of providing assistance to failing schools may be one to consider.

A re-evaluation of the value of mental health inquiry reports is indicated, not least because many of the findings are repeated in successive reports suggesting that policy makers and practitioners are not learning from previous inquiries. Is this because the findings of reports are not easily available and/or assimilated or because the inquiry process, instead of encouraging learning, promotes resistance to integrating the information in some way? Have people become saturated by the number and frequency of inquiries, making it difficult to hear what changes are needed? In some cases those professionals involved may feel they have been scape-goated to divert attention from the overall service management. It is undoubtedly the case that, however competent a practitioner one is ultimately considered to be, the inquiry process is traumatic and often destructive for those involved.

The cost is diverting resources away from service provision. Many argue that, while inquiries may have had a value, they have ceased to serve a useful function. 'There is a feeling that they have become so common that their impact has diminished accordingly' (Howlett, 1997, p183). Mental health service providers are facing a surfeit of reports and it is unsatisfactory if each health authority or provider unit has to have its own tragedy in order to learn how to improve services. Research into the outcomes of child abuse inquiries does not offer much optimism for hoping that the inquiry process will ensure the necessary change (Reder & Duncan, 1996). Yet at the very least, some of the lessons from the child abuse inquiries of the 1970s and 80s could be integrated into mental health services so that a mechanism similar to that of the area child protection committee is developed in order to investigate and learn from future community care tragedies without the disadvantages of the public independent inquiry.

Communication
One of the most consistent findings of virtually every inquiry into the failings and tragedies of our care for the severely mentally ill in the community is the need to improve communication, both within and between agencies and with families and carers. This is also one of the main findings of the inquiry into homicides and suicides (Boyd, 1996 p8). Safe practice and the successful management of risk in the community require people to work co-operatively, to share information, to clarify and review care plans, reassess the risks, and so on. Yet repeatedly liaison and interagency working are found to be less than satisfactory. This must lead us to question what inhibits the process. The frequency and complexity of the problem suggest that there is no simple solution. Effective systems need to be in place which facilitate communication between professionals and agencies. But, although structural change may be indicated to put policies and procedures in place to ensure appropriate levels of information sharing and consultation, there

needs to be a more imaginative response to achieving good practice. Assertive outreach and follow-up are more than a monitoring process. 'Continuity of care and of staying in touch' is a recurring theme as tragedies are investigated retrospectively (Reed, 1997).

Many inquiries emphasise the incomplete implementation of the Care Programme Approach as a causal factor to account for the breakdown in care – for example, Newby (1995), NG (1996) Stoker (1996), Taylor (1996), Mursell (1997). The Joughin Report (1997) goes further, saying that the fact that the CPA does not exist in the Isle of Man was fundamental to the tragedy it investigated. However, structures on their own are not enough. In Wales, where there is no CPA, is the quality of community care significantly diminished? What is important is good practice. This requires adequate and continuing training and professional as well as organisational will. By looking at inquiry reports over a period of time there are signs that some things are changing as a result of such investigations, as well as the more usual criticism that the same mistakes are being made. For example, the inquiry following the death of Isabel Schwarz, a social worker (Campbell, 1988), recommended that a system of aftercare should be in place, which has now come to be called the CPA, and the inquiry into the death of Jonathan Zito (Clunis, 1994) led to the setting up of supervision registers. However, a note of caution is warranted here. It is dangerous to rely too heavily on registers because better monitoring alone can lead to a false sense of security.

It is time to re-evaluate the role and tasks of the keyworker, which means at the very least some investment in training workshops, good supervision, and recognition by managers that effective interagency working is time consuming. Howlett talks of a basic level of care requiring 'an effective key worker relationship with individual patients, 24-hour crisis intervention services and adequate provision of secure beds when treatment is needed' (Howlett, 1997, p175). It may be that achieving representative attendance at CPA and Section 117 meetings is an unattainable goal, particularly if such meetings need to be held at short notice because of someone's deteriorating mental health. Yet the reports demonstrate that multidisciplinary discussion is fundamental to understanding and managing those most at risk of breakdown. Might it be more cost effective to install telephone conferencing facilities for example? Should the keyworker be more proactive in contacting each team member individually by telephone on a regular basis? Certainly more communication could take place by fax for example. The multidisciplinary team should consider the venues for meetings carefully. By way of illustration, if obtaining a GP's attendance proves difficult, holding the meeting at the GP's surgery may be a solution. What seems to be necessary is for the issue to be properly addressed by mental health agencies, to examine how much time is required and exactly what is involved in managing risk through effective co-operative working. Imaginative solutions to problems need to be sought. Additionally, for problems which continue to defy solution we need to take a more radical approach to identifying the root causes of them. Until we understand the underlying causes for poor communication, it is unlikely that the recommendations of inquiries will be readily translated into action.

Risk and hindsight bias
It is always easy after a homicide to decide that greater attention should have been given to that particular patient. Similarly, it is always possible to conclude that the level of provision was in some way inadequate. However, targeting scarce resources accurately in advance is much trickier. From my own practice it seems clear that as risk increases so does anxiety. The greater the concern expressed, the more paper is generated, and the number of professional workers involved expands in an effort to contain the anxiety. Although most inquiries conclude that the fatal event could not have been prevented or predicted, very often there were warning signs and clear indications that all was not well.

However, the bias of hindsight needs to be kept in mind. While professional skill in assessing risk can be improved, it must also be acknowledged that the success achieved by mental health services can never meet public expectations. Society insists on an absolute guarantee that there is no risk, but unfortunately there can be no absolutes. For people who may have suffered from severe mental health problems to realise their potential, and achieve a quality of life in the community, risks have to be taken. But from society's viewpoint there is no such thing as an acceptable degree of risk. It is right that professional practice is challenged and that service provision is developed to minimise risk as far as possible. But it also has to be recognised that there will always have to be an element of risk taking.

The transfer of large numbers of hospital patients to the community requires creative services which are designed to meet individual need. Inquiry reports indicate there is no room for complacency, and all mental health professionals must continue to strive to improve their practice. Resource implications must be addressed. According to Boyd, providing 'high quality community work will usually be more expensive of time and money than similar work carried out in a hospital' (Boyd, 1996, p63). However, resources alone will not solve the complexities facing service providers. The problems are multifaceted and as such need comprehensive responses.

Services for people with learning difficulties
While this book has focused almost exclusively on mental health services, the implications for the safe management of risk in providing community services for people with learning difficulties should not be overlooked. The Doherty (1995), Stoker (1996) and Holland (1997) inquiries in particular are concerned with services for people with learning difficulties. Such services present particular problems for agencies in managing risk. However, the implications for policy and practice are broadly transferable to services for people with learning difficulties, particularly if there is a history of challenging behaviour or violence. Respecting individual rights regardless of the difficulties a person's illness or behaviour may present is central to quality community care. But respect for individuals must be balanced by respect for other people so as to prevent harm to others. As Tindall points out, 'a successful risk management process should be to maximise opportunities for people with learning difficulties to take risks' (Tindall, 1997, p107). He talks about this being an essentially positive and creative process rather than a reactive one.

The challenge for community care
Society's acceptance of people with serious mental health problems or learning difficulties requires there to be confidence that appropriate levels of community support and skilled intervention for those who need it will be available. The balance between individual freedom and public safety will always be a difficult one to maintain with accuracy and sensitivity. This, though, is the challenge for everyone who is committed to improving the quality of services in community care.

But how do we face this challenge? What does it mean for mental health professionals? What does it mean for service users? What are the implications for services and for the wider community? Because many of the inquiries focus on circumstances involving people who have hitherto been recipients of 'ordinary' mental health services and who have had no previous contact with forensic services, many of the implications for services apply to general psychiatric services as opposed to specialised forensic ones.

Aside from the problems associated with mental illness, increasingly the incidence and extent of domestic violence are being recognised as a significant problem which needs addressing. Similarly, in recent years society's awareness of child abuse, both physical and sexual, has increased dramatically, perhaps partly as a consequence of the child protection inquiries into tragic incidents which took place in the community as the numbers of children placed in residential care declined. The scandals of child abuse in the community led to concerted efforts on the part of service providers to ensure that the risk of harm to children was minimised. Yet initially the extent of the problem of child abuse was not readily accepted. Perhaps, therefore, given that many mental health inquiries are concerned with people who have not previously come to the attention of the forensic services, services should be alerted to the possible existence of violence in a way which we have hitherto tended to want to avoid. The evidence suggesting an increased risk of violence in a small but significant group of the total population of people suffering from a severe mental illness is stated clearly in the review of recent research presented by Howlett (1997).

Publicising scandals creates an immediate imperative to get services right. In the 1960s and 70s scandals in large hospitals for the care of people suffering from mental illness and learning difficulties were the precursor to many changes in the way care is delivered, not least the present policy of care in the community. Now, by focusing attention on community services for the mentally ill, service deficits can be addressed to make the necessary improvements a reality. Despite the current pressure to increase the number of secure hospital beds in the mental health system, the principles of care for the mentally disordered offender as expressed so clearly in Reed's review of services for mentally disordered offenders still underpin and guide the planning and development of services. 'Patients should be cared for as far as possible, in the community, rather than in institutional settings, under conditions of no greater security than is justified by the degree of danger they present to themselves or to others' (Department of Health and Home Office, 1992, p40). It is unlikely that the present policy of placing people in the community will be reversed on a large scale basis. But as people continue to stay in the community rather than be admitted to hospital, so the risk increases.

Therefore, as mental health professionals we have to be much clearer about what we are doing and why. We need to be open about risk assessment, and responsive to people's needs for services. Too often in the past resources have not been adequate to make services work. By using the recommendations from successive inquiry reports, it becomes very clear that there are no short cuts to good community-based services. There needs to be a range of services available, including 24-hour care, seven days a week. Although there is often talk of a seamless service, what this must be made to mean in reality is not using boundaries to restrict a person's access to a service he or she requires.

The message from the inquiries is clear. It is no longer acceptable to 'pass the buck', or to hand over to carers for whom the burden of providing continuous care is too great. Carers have their own needs and are entitled to have those needs independently assessed and appropriate provision made. Social workers must be assertive in their endeavours to ensure there is a whole range of community services with the necessary links with health service provision. They must also be confident about their own contribution in multidisciplinary team work. Likewise doctors need to be more responsive to relatives and carers, by being more prepared to listen and take note of their concerns. Similarly, nurses who are very good at seeing their patient as an individual with rights, need to be more aware of their patient's social and economic context, thus seeing also the needs of the community.

Endnote

I hope that this book can be used in a number of different ways to empower people to campaign for and promote, through their own practice, better services for those receiving community care who suffer from a severe mental illness. According to inquiries, tragedies in community care occur for many reasons, but particularly because insufficient attention is paid to risk and because there is poor communication on a variety of different levels. Community care as a policy remains sound. But it is not a static policy. Over time it evolves as our level of knowledge and understanding increases. Services need to continue to be developed accordingly.

We must develop our skills of engaging with people in difficulty and understanding their needs. Services must be responsive to those needs and must be delivered sensitively and imaginatively. For the majority of people who experience severe mental health problems, with an adequate level of service and support they are able to live and contribute as full members of society. But what inquiry reports repeatedly tell us is that there is no room for complacency and enormous scope for improvement. Therefore this book seeks to outline some of the important findings for improving practice. It aims to provide a comprehensive guide to some of the recent mental health inquiries into the failings of community care. The purpose behind providing complete sets of recommendations is so that they can and indeed should be used to inform practice both now and in the future. Because of their status as recommendations they provide individual workers with the evidence they need to secure improvements in the way services are delivered.

In my own practice I have used inquiries extensively to inform my own decision making not only as a manager and trainer but also with service users. It is often far easier, for example, to use a case vignette from a published report to explain to patients why they need to disclose information about their index offence and risk to another agency such as a housing department or hostel, for whom such information is vital to ensure that appropriate packages of care can be not only offered, but also managed safely.

If we ignore the lessons, so powerfully conveyed through the succession of inquiries, the outcome will be further tragedy, more suffering, and more deaths. Community care should be about caring for people, people who have a history of vulnerability and illness. It is not primarily about saving money by closing hospitals. Quality service cannot be provided cheaply, but if we do not deliver proper levels of care in the community, the demand for more secure hospital beds with their attendant costs will continue to increase. Within our own sphere of mental health service provision we can all improve our own practice by being better informed as a result of the inquiry reports published. Ignoring such reports is not an option, and is both professionally and morally indefensible.

List of Abbreviations

ASW	Approved Social Worker
AWOL	Absent Without Leave
C3 Division	Mental Health Unit, Home Office – mental health section responsible for restricted patient cases
CCETSW	Central Council for Education and Training in Social Work
CPA	Care Programme Approach
CMHN	Community Mental Health Nurse
CMHT	Community Mental Health Team
CMHW	Community Mental Health Worker
CPN	Community Psychiatric Nurse
CPS	Crown Prosecution Service
CSN	Community Support Nurse
DHSS	Department of Health and Social Security
DSS	Department of Social Security
DoH	Department of Health
DSH	deliberate self-harm
DVLA	Driver and Vehicle Licensing Agency
GP	General Practitioner (family doctor)
IMR	Inmate Medical Record
LMC	Local Medical Committee
MHA	Mental Health Act

MHAC	Mental Health Act Commission
MHLT	Mental Health Locality Team
MHRT	Mental Health Review Tribunal
NHS	National Health Service
NHSE	National Health Service Executive
OT	Occupational Therapist
OTA	Occupational Therapy Assistant
RMO	Responsible Medical Officer
S. 117	Section 117 Aftercare (Mental Health Act 1983)
SSD	Social Services Department
SSI	Social Services Inspectorate
UKCC	United Kingdom Central Council for Nursing, Midwifery and Health Visiting

Bibliography

Armstrong Inquiry (1996). *Report of the Inquiry into the Care and Treatment of Shaun Anthony Armstrong*. (Chair, C. J. Freeman.) Middlesbrough, Tees District Health Authority.

Barratt Inquiry (1991). *Regional Fact Finding Committee of Enquiry into the Admission, Care, Treatment and Discharge of Carol Barratt* (Chair, Cyril Unwin.) Nottingham, Trent Health Authority.

Blackwood Inquiry (1993). *Report of the Committee of Inquiry into the Death of Orville Blackwood and a Review of the Deaths of Two Other Afro-Caribbean Patients 'Big, Black and Dangerous?'* (Chair, Professor Herschel Prins.) London, Special Hospitals Service Authority.

Blom-Cooper, L (1992). *Report of the Committee of Inquiry into Complaints about Ashworth Hospital* (Chair, Louis Blom-Cooper.) (Cm 2028). London, HMSO.

Blom-Cooper, L (1995). *The Falling Shadow – One Patient's Mental Health Care 1978- 1993 – Report of the Committee of Inquiry into the events leading up to and surrounding the fatal incident at the Edith Morgan Centre, Torbay on 1 September 1993* (Chair, Louis Blom-Cooper.) London, Duckworth.

Blom-Cooper, L (1996). *The Case of Jason Mitchell: Report of the Independent Panel of Inquiry* (Chair, Louis Blom-Cooper.) London, Duckworth.

Boland Inquiry (1995). *Independent Panel of Inquiry into the circumstances surrounding the Deaths of Ellen and Alan Boland* (Chair, Mrs J. Hughes.) London, City of Westminster, Kensington, Chelsea and Westminster Health Authorities, and the North West London Mental Health NHS Trust.

Boyd, W (1996). *Report of the Confidential Inquiry into Homicides and Suicides by Mentally Ill People* (Director, Dr William Boyd.) London, Royal College of Psychiatrists.

Buchanan Inquiry (1994). *The Report of the Independent Panel of Inquiry examining the Case of Michael Buchanan* (Chair, Christopher Heginbotham.) London, North West London Mental Health Trust.

Burton Inquiry (1996). *Report of the Independent Inquiry into the Treatment and Care of Richard John Burton* (Chair, Hugh Chapman.) Leicester, Leicestershire Health Authority.

Campbell Inquiry (1988). *Report of the Committee of Inquiry into the Care and After-care of Miss Sharon Campbell* (Chair, John Spokes QC.) (Cm 440). London, HMSO.

Carers (Recognition and Services) Act 1995. London, HMSO.

Carr Report (1997). *Report of the Inquiry into the Treatment and Care of Darren Carr* (Chair, Professor Genevra Richardson.) Reading, Berkshire Health Authority, Berkshire County Council, Oxfordshire Health Authority and Oxfordshire County Council.

Carson, D (1996). 'Structural Problems, Perspectives and Solutions.' In: Peay, J. (Ed) *Inquiries after Homicide*. London, Duckworth.

Clunis Inquiry (1994). *The Report of the Inquiry into the Care and Treatment of Christopher Clunis* (Chair, Jean Ritchie QC.) London, HMSO.

Cooper, G (1996). Rosie report a 'whitewash'. *The Independent*, 14 June 1996.

Department of Health (1990). *The Care Programme Approach for people with a mental illness referred to the specialist psychiatric services HC(90)23/LASSL(90)11.* London, Department of Health.

Department of Health (1992) *Review of Health and Social Services for Mentally Disordered Offenders and Others Requiring Similar Services.* (Chair, Dr John Reed.) Final Summary Report Cm 2088. London. HMSO.

Department of Health and Welsh Office (1993). *Code of Practice – Mental Health Act 1983(2nd edition)* London, HMSO.

Department of Health (1994a). *The Health of the Nation Mental Illness Key Area Handbook (2nd edition)* London, HMSO.

Department of Health (1994b). *Introduction of supervision registers for mentally ill people from 1 April 1994 HSG(94)5*. London, Department of Health.

Department of Health (1995). *Building Bridges – A guide to arrangements for inter-agency working for the care and protection of severely mentally ill people* London, Department of Health.

Doherty Inquiry (1995). *Report of the Inquiry Team to the Western Health and Social Services Board* (Chair, Professor George Fenton). Londonderry, Western Health and Social Services Board.

DU Inquiry (1993). *Report of the Inquiry Panel to Investigate the Serious Untoward Incident at the Tudor Rest Home, West Bridgford, on the night of 3rd/4th August 1993* (Chair, Mrs P Turnbull.) Nottingham, Nottingham Health Authority.

Eastman, N (1996). 'Towards an Audit of Inquiries.' In: Peay, J. (Ed) *Inquiries after Homicide* London, Duckworth.

Elliott, A (1992) *Hidden Children*, Mental Health Development Section, Leeds Social Services Department.

Grey Report (1995). *Report of the Independent Team into the Care and Treatment of Kenneth Grey to East London and the City Health Authority* (Chair, Jane Mishcon.) London, East London & the City Health Authority.

Grounds, A (1995). 'Risk Assessment and Management in Clinical Context.' In: Crichton J (Ed) *Psychiatric Patient Violence – Risk and Response* London, Duckworth.

Hampshire Report (1996). *Report of the Independent Inquiry Team into the Care and Treatment of Francis Hampshire to Redbridge and Waltham Forest Health Authority* (Chair, Jane Mishcon.) London, Redbridge and Waltham Forest Health Authority.

Harry Inquiry (1994). *Inquiry into the Deaths of Jason and Natalia Harry (summary report)* (Chair, Jean Gabbott.) London, Haringey Area Child Protection Committee.

Holland Inquiry (1997). *Report of the Independent Panel of Inquiry into the circumstances surrounding the absconsion of Mr Holland from the care of Horizon NHS Trust on 29 August 1996* (Chair, Professor Herschel Prins.) London, Horizon NHS Trust.

Howell Inquiry (1997). *Report of the Inquiry into the Events Leading to the Death of David Howell* (Chair, Dr Jacky Chambers.) Birmingham, Birmingham Health Authority and Birmingham City Council.

Howlett, M (1997). 'Community Care Homicide Inquiries and Risk Assessment'. In: Kemshall and Pritchard (eds) *Good Practice in Risk Assessment and Risk Management 2: Protection, Rights and Responsibilities*. London, Jessica Kingsley.

Independent, The (5 August 1997, p2). *Victim's mother sues for negligence.*

Johnston, P (1997). 'Throughcare Practice, Risk and Contact with Victims'. In: Kemshall and Pritchard (eds) *Good Practice in Risk Assessment and Risk Management 2: Protection, Rights and Responsibilities.* London, Jessica Kingsley.

Joughin Report (1997). *Practice, Planning and Partnership – The Lessons to be Learned from the case of Susan Patricia Joughin.* A Report to the Council of Ministers of the Isle of Man Government Volume 1, Douglas, Isle of Man Government.

Kemshall, H and Pritchard, J (eds) (1996). *Good Practice in Risk Assessment and Risk Management.* London, Jessica Kingsley.

Kemshall, H and Pritchard, J (eds) (1997). *Good Practice in Risk Assessment and Risk Management 2 Protection, Rights and Responsibilities.* London, Jessica Kingsley.

Kirkman Inquiry (1991). *Report of the Panel of Inquiry Appointed to Investigate the Case of Kim Kirkman* (Chair, Dr Donald Dick.) Birmingham, West Midlands Regional Health Authority.

Kopernik-Steckel Inquiry (1997). *Report of the Inquiry into the Treatment and Care of Gilbert Kopernik-Steckel* (Chair, Jeffrey Greenwell.) Croydon, Croydon Health Authority.

Mabota Report (1996). *Report of the Independent Inquiry Team into the Care and Treatment of Kumbi Mabota* (Chair, Derek Holwill.) London, Redbridge and Waltham Forest Health Authority.

Martin, J P (1984). *Hospitals in Trouble.* London, Blackwell.

McFadden Inquiry (1995). *Report of the Inquiry into the Care and Treatment of Philip McFadden* (Chair, Dr James Dyer.) Edinburgh, Mental Welfare Commission for Scotland.

Mental Health Act (1983). London, HMSO.

Mental Health Act Commission (1997) *Seventh Biennial Report, 1995-1997.* Norwich, Stationery Office.

Mental Health (Patients in the Community) Act 1995. London, HMSO.

Mursell Report (March 1997). *The Report into the Care and Treatment of Martin Mursell* (Chair, Lincoln Crawford.) London, Camden & Islington Health Authority.

Newby Report (1995). *Report of the Inquiry into the circumstances leading to the death of Jonathan Newby (a volunteer worker) on 9th October 1993 in Oxford* (Chair, Nicola Davies QC.) Oxford, Oxfordshire Health Authority.

NG Inquiry (1996). *Report of the Independent Inquiry Team into the Care and Treatment of NG* (Chair, J. R. Main QC.) London, Ealing, Hammersmith & Hounslow Health Authority and London Borough of Hounslow.

NHS and Community Care Act 1990. London, HMSO.

NHS Executive (1994). *Guidance on the discharge of mentally disordered people and their continuing care in the community (HSG(94)27/LASSL (94)4)* London, Department of Health.

Nicholson, R (Chair) (1996). *Learning Lessons: Report into the events leading to the incident at St John's Way Medical Centre in December 1995*. London, Camden & Islington Health Authority.

Payne, M (1996). *What is Professional Social Work?* Birmingham, Venture.

Petch, E and Bradley, C (1997) 'Learning the lessons from homicide inquiries: adding insult to injury?' *Journal of Forensic Psychiatry* 8(1), pp161-184.

Prins, H (1995) *Offenders, Deviants or Patients?* 2nd Edition, London, Routledge.

Radcliffe, M (1997) *Nursing Times* 93(12), p23.

Reder, P and Duncan, S (1996). 'Reflections on Child Abuse Inquiries.' In: Peay, J (Ed) *Inquiries after Homicide*. London, Duckworth.

Reed, J (1997) 'Risk Assessment and Clinical Risk Management: the lessons from recent Inquiries.' *British Journal of Psychiatry* 170 (suppl. 32), pp4-7.

Rock, P (1996). 'The Inquiry and Victims Families.' In: Peay, J (Ed) *Inquiries after Homicide*. London, Duckworth.

Rooney Inquiry (1992). *Independent Inquiry Kevin Rooney* (Chair, Andrew Collins QC.) London, North East Thames Health Authority.

Shepherd, G (1995). 'Care and Control in the Community.' In: Crichton, J (Ed) *Psychiatric Patient Violence – Risk and Response*. London, Duckworth.

Sheppard, D (1996). *Learning the Lessons*. London, Zito Trust.

Sheppard, D. and Edwards, P. (1997) *Institute of Mental Health Law*. http://www: imhl. com.

Sinclair Inquiry (1996). *Report of the Inquiry into the Treatment and Care of Raymond Sinclair* (Chair, Richard Lingham.) Kent, West Kent Health Authority and Kent County Council Social Services.

Smith Inquiry (1996). *Report of the Inquiry into the Care of Anthony Smith* (Chair, Professor Sir John Wood.) Derbyshire, Southern Derbyshire Health Authority and Derbyshire County Council.

Smith Report (1997). *Report of the Independent Panel of Inquiry into the Care and Treatment of Paul Smith* (Chair, Jane Mishcon.) Peterborough, North West Anglia Health Authority.

Stoker Inquiry (1996). *Report to Northumberland Health Authority of the Independent Inquiry Team into the Care and Treatment of Richard Stoker* (Chair, A G Brown.) Northumberland, Northumberland Health Authority.

Taylor Inquiry 'Caring for the Carer' (1996). *Report of Committee of Inquiry to Tees Health Authority.* (Chair, Richard Barlow.) Tees Health Authority.

Tindall, B (1997) 'People with Learning Difficulties – Citizenship, Personal Development and the Management of Risk.' In Kemshall, H and Pritchard, J (eds) *Good Practice in Risk Assessment amd Risk Management 2 Protection, Rights and Responsibilities*. London, Jessica Kingsley.

Viner Report (1996). *The Report of the Independent Inquiry into the circumstances surrounding the deaths of Robert and Muriel Viner* (Chair, Anthony Harbour.) Dorset, Dorset Health Commission.

Woodley Report (1995). *The Woodley Team Report* (Chair, Len Woodley QC.) London, East London & The City Health Authority and Newham Council.

Index to Recommendations in Inquiry Reports

(listed by recommendation number)

community mental health worker Mursell 15, (p128);

community psychiatric nurse (CPN) Campbell 27, (p20); Clunis 38, 39, (p37); Buchanan 1, 10, 11, 12, 13, 14, (pp45-47); Robinson 12, (p51); Boland 11, (p55); Doherty 14, (p76); Viner 4, (p84); NG 13, (p96); Hampshire 4, 18, 19, 20, (pp98-100); Smith 17, 18, 19, 54, 55, (pp114-117); Stoker 1, (p120); Mursell 15, (p128); see also Community Mental Health Nurse (CMHN) and Community Mental Health Worker

community psychiatric service DU 8, 9, 11, (p30); Clunis 20, (p35); Doherty 5, (p75); see also mental health service

competencies Mabota 5, (p108); Smith 18, 19, (p114); see also core competence

complaints Newby 9.2, 9.5, (pp61-62); Woodley 14, (p68);

compliance including non-compliance Clunis 9, 29,(pp34-36); Harry 16, (p44); Robinson 13, (p51); NG 7, (p96); Hampshire 12, 13, 15, (p100); Armstrong 12, (p103); Smith 10, (p113); Mursell 10, 14, (p128); see also relapse

compulsory admission Robinson 14, (p51); Doherty 22, (p77);

compulsory supervision Doherty 16, (p77);

conditional discharge Kirkman 5, 6, (p24); Stoker 1, 9, (pp120-121);

confidentiality Kirkman 6, 8, (pp24-25); Clunis 19, 37, 40, 62, (pp35-39); Robinson 12, 22, (pp51-52); Boland 13, (p55); Newby 11, (p63); Woodley 20, 21, 22, 33, 34, (pp69-71); Viner 3, 17, (pp84-86); Mitchell 35, (p93); Taylor 9, (p111); Smith 31, 35, (p115);

consultant psychiatrist Campbell 26, 27, (pp19-20); Clunis 2, 5, 9, 16, 65, (pp34-40); Harry 17, (p44); Boland 1, 2, (p53); Newby 10.2, (p62); Woodley 35, 43, (pp71-72); Doherty 1, 2, 3, (p75); NG 3, 11, 15, (p95-97); Hampshire 10, (p99); Sinclair 2, 3, 4, 5, 10, (pp105-106); Smith 21, 39, (pp114-116); Stoker 1, 2, 8, (pp120-121); Learning Lessons 1, 9, (p123); see also psychiatrist

contrary to medical advice Doherty 3, 4, 22, (pp75-77);

control Barratt 3, (p21);

co-operation Clunis 12, (p35); see also liaison

co-ordination see liaison and keyworker

core competence Newby 3.3, 3.4, (p59); see also competencies

counselling Campbell 10, 11, 12, (p18); Woodley 48, 49, 50, (p72); Hampshire 5, 6, 7, (p98); Mabota 10, (p108); Smith 28, 29, 30, 31, 32, 33, 34, 35, 36, (p115); Learning Lessons 20, (p124);

empowerment Woodley 31, (p70);

enhanced hospital order Buchanan 20, 21, 23, (pp47-48);

ethical committee Boland 14, (p55);

ethnic minority groups Campbell 29, 30, (p20); Clunis 78, 79, 80, (pp40-41); Harry 10, 11, 18, (pp43-44); Woodley 10, 40, 54, 60, 62, (pp67-74);

evaluation Barratt 5, (p21);

failure to attend appointments see compliance

family see relatives and carers

Family Health Services Authority Clunis 73, (p41); Woodley 52, (p73);

fax machines Clunis 72, (p40);

forensic psychiatrist Clunis 57, (p39); Woodley 35, (p71); Doherty 11, 13, (p76); Mitchell 6, 27, (pp89-92);

forensic psychiatric services Kirkman 7, 9, (pp24-25); Clunis 57, (p39); Woodley 45, (p72); Mitchell 27, 28, 29, 41, 46, (pp92-94); Sinclair 8, (p105);

forensic social work Mitchell 25, 45, (pp92-94);

friend Clunis 21, (p36); Woodley 9, (p67); Smith 8, (p113);   see also befriender, carer and relative

funding Clunis 36, (p37); Newby 8.5, (p61); Woodley 9, 26, 52, 54, 56, 57, 58, 59, (pp67-74); Mitchell 26, 40, (pp92-93);

General Medical Council Mitchell 35, (p93);

general practitioners Campbell 24, 27, (pp19-20); Rooney 1, 3, (p27-28); DU 8, 9, 10, 11, 12, 13, 14, 16, (pp30-31); Clunis 70, 71, 72, 73, 74, (pp40-41); Boland 1, 8, 14, (pp53-55); McFadden 1, 2, (pp64-65); Viner 2, 3, 4, (p84); NG 4, (p95); Hampshire 18, 19, 20, (p100); Armstrong 7, (p102); Smith 21, 30, 33, (pp114-115); Burton 4, (p119); Stoker 4, (p121); Learning Lessons 11, 13, 14, 15, 16, 17, 18, 19, 20, (pp124-125);

GP fundholders Woodley 52, (p73);

Government Woodley 26, 59, (pp69-74); Mitchell 25, 33, 36, (pp92-93);

guidance/guidelines Campbell 7, 8, 10, 14, (pp7-18); Kirkman 7, 16, (pp24-26); DU 1, 2, 15, 20, (pp29-31); Harry 6, (p43); Buchanan 12, 22, (pp46-48); Boland 10, 13, 18, 24, (pp54-56); Newby 5, 11, (pp59-63); Woodley 5, 33,

procedures Kirkman 10, (p25); Rooney 3, (p28); Clunis 58, (p39); Harry 11,13, (p44); Robinson 3, (p51); Boland 15, 16, 19, 20, 23, 25, (pp55-56); Woodley 33, 41, (pp70-71); Doherty 8, (p76); Grey 16, 17, 29, (pp80-82); Viner 5, 13, 18, 20, 26, 27, (pp84-87); Mitchell 15, (p90); NG 9, 10, (p96); Sinclair 12, (p106); Mahota 1, 2, 3, 4, (p108); Burton 1, 2, 3, (p118); Stoker 9, (p121); Mursell 2,13, (pp127-128); see also policy and protocol

protocol Robinson 7, (p51); Woodley 35, (p71); Viner 20, (p86); Stoker 5, (p121); Learning Lessons 2, 4, (p123); see also policy and procedure

providers Mitchell 41, (p93); Learning Lessons 23, 27, (p125); Mursell 23, (p129);

psychiatric service Clunis 35, 38, 58, 73, 76, (pp37-41); McFadden 2, (pp64-65); Mitchell 44, (p93); Hampshire 4, (p100); Armstrong 7, (p102);

psychiatrist/psychiatry Campbell 3, (p17); Kirkman 8, 18, (pp25-26); Clunis 2, (p34); Harry 6, (p43); Buchanan 27, (p49); Woodley 5, 37, (pp67-71); Mitchell 1, 27, 28, 29, (pp89-92); Hampshire 19, (p100); Armstrong 2, (p102);

psychodynamic approaches/psychotherapy Buchanan 20, (p47); Mitchell 14, 29, 42, (pp91-93);

psychology/psychologists Campbell 24, 27, (pp19-20); Buchanan 20, 21, (pp47-48); Mitchell 7, 15, 26, (pp89-92);

psychological dimension/problem Boland 3, 5, (p54);

psychometric tests Kirkman 4, (p24);

psychopath Kirkman 18, (p26);

psychotherapy Buchanan 20, (p47); see also psychodynamic approaches

public Rooney 5, (pp28-29); Clunis 17, 22, 81, (pp35-41); Buchanan 21, (p48); Robinson 12, 22, (pp51-52); Boland 22, (p56); Newby 2, (p58); Woodley 21, (p69); Doherty 24, 25, (p77);

public inquiry Mitchell 32, 33, (p92);

public interest Kirkman 5, (p24);

purchasers/purchasing authority Mitchell 40, 41, 43, 44, 45, (pp93-94); Sinclair 2, (p105); Mursell 23, (p129); see also commissioning authority

quality assurance Woodley 41, 43, (pp71-72); Mitchell 41, 43, (p93); Armstrong 14, (p103);

race Harry 10, 11, (pp43-44);

recall to hospital Clunis 29, (p36); Harry 16, (p44);

record(s), recording Campbell 1, 2, 4, 6, 14, (pp16-18); DU 16, 18, (p31); Clunis 3, 16, 18, 41, 50, (pp34-38); Robinson 5, 6, (p50); Boland 1, 2, 7, 16, 19, (pp53-56); Newby 3.1, 4, (pp58-59); Woodley 6, 22, (pp67-69); Doherty 5, 6, 7, 9, (pp75-76); Grey 3, 4, 8, 9, 10, 19, (pp79-81); Viner 7, 9, (pp84-85); Mitchell 2, 8, 35, 38, 44, (pp89-93); NG 4, 5, 6, 7, 8, 9, 10, 13, 17, (pp95-97); Hampshire 9, 17, 18, 19, 20, (pp98-100); Armstrong 1, 2, 3, (p102); Sinclair 6, 7, 9, 10, (pp105-106); Mabota 1, 2, (p107); Smith 5, 8, 10, 12, 15, 27, 44, (pp113-116); Burton 1, 2, 3, 4, (pp118-119); Stoker 3, 6, (pp120-121); Mursell 6, 7, 9, 10, 12, 16, (pp127-129);

regional secure unit see secure unit

Registered Homes Act 1984 Newby 5, (p59);

registers Campbell 26,(p19); Clunis 19, 74, (pp35-41); Viner 14, (p85); Sinclair 12, (p106); Smith 36, (p117); see also supervision registers and Section 117 Register

rehabilitation Campbell 27, (p20); Clunis 52, (p38); Buchanan 4, (p46); Woodley 9, 32, (pp67-70); Viner 1, 11, (pp83-85); Smith 6, 47, (pp113-116);

relapse Clunis 8, 10, 17, 29, (pp34-36); Buchanan 14, (p47); Robinson 13, (p51); NG 7, (p96); see also compliance

relatives Clunis 8, 21, 32, (pp34-37); Robinson 10, 11, (p51); Boland 4, (p54); Woodley 9, (p67); Hampshire 6, 7, 11, 15, 16, (pp98-100); Sinclair 9, (pp105-106); Smith 1, 7, 8, 41, (pp112-116); see also carers and friend

report Campbell 15, (p18); Barratt 1, 13, (pp21-22); Clunis 50, (p38); Doherty 24, 25, (p77); Grey 3, 29, 30, (pp79-82); Viner 32, (p87); Mitchell 1, 8, 37, (pp89-93); Stoker 3, (p120); Learning Lessons 28, (p125); see also internal inquiry

research Kirkman 11, 21, (pp25-26);

residential care Newby 10.2, (pp62-63); Mitchell 40, (p93);

residential home DU 5, (p30); Newby 4, (p59);

resources Clunis 51, 52, 53, 54, 55, 56, 57, (pp38-39); Harry 2, (p43); Buchanan 24, (p48); Boland 11, 17, (p55); Newby 10.1, 10.2, (pp62-63); Woodley 52, 53, 54, 55, 56, 57, 58, 59, 60, 61, 62, 63, (pp73-74); Viner 12, (p85);

Author Index

(The Chair and panel members of Inquiry Panels are listed in the author index, but all references to reports are contained within the subject and recommendation indexes).

Subject Index

(see also the recommendation index for references contained
within recommendations)

outpatient appointment/clinic/services 53, 63, 65, 83, 101, 111, 118, 138, 139, 152, 186, 188, 191

outreach services 158, 201

Oxfordshire Health Authority 57

Palmer Rosie 9, 13, 101, 197

parents 50 see also relatives and carers

personality disorder/psychopathic disorder 7, 23, 27, 44, 47, 65, 74, 101, 117, 118, 122, 151, 180

police 7, 31, 33, 39, 42, 43, 44, 51, 64, 101, 107, 142, 146, 154, 168, 184

policy 2, 3, 5, 15, 23, 138, 143, 148, 149, 150, 152, 154, 171, 172, 174, 175, 178, 179, 181, 195, 197, 199, 200

poverty 104, 119, 144

prison 3, 23, 48, 53, 66, 78, 101, 104, 107, 146, 187, 188, 198

prison medical officers 48

private sector 31, 146, 158

probation service/probation officers 2, 31, 44, 48, 53, 75, 79, 94, 119, 120, 135, 142, 154, 186-190, 198

procedures 143, 152, 153, 154, 156, 171, 172, 177, 178, 200

psychiatric history 132 see also history

psychiatry/psychiatrist 2, 31, 39, 118, 138, 163-172, 175, 186, 187 see also consultant psychiatrist and responsible medical officer

psychology/psychological treatments 2, 46, 47, 190

psychopathy see personality disorder

psychosis 98, 109, 122, 145, 167,170

psychotherapy 46

public safety 1, 4, 5, 51, 131, 133, 163, 186, 188, 203

Race/ethnicity 2, 3, 16, 33, 40, 41, 42, 43, 66, 143-148, 172, 180, 189 see also ethnic minorities

racism 40, 144, 145, 146, 147 see also institutional racism

recall to hospital 120

records/recording 49, 132, 133, 136, 142, 146, 170, 173, 177, 178, 185-186, 189

Redbridge and Waltham Forest Health Authority 97, 106

rehabilitation 23, 66, 119

relapse 16, 27, 33, 45, 50, 94, 98, 119, 126, 139, 141, 161, 166, 173, 184, 185, 188, 190, 191, 201

relatives 119, 136, 137, 138, 139, 140, 141, 142, 151, 159, 198 see also family and carers

research 23, 142

residential care/home 29, 45, 65, 104, 120, 160, 161, 192, 203

resources 4, 37, 122, 142, 143, 155, 181, 195, 197, 200, 204

Responsible Medical Officer (RMO) 21, 40, 119, 163-172, 177, 191

restriction order 15, 23, 27, 49, 88, 109, 117, 120, 168

review 148, 155, 185, 187, 200